BRAND NU

THE BEST OF NEW BLACK WRITING

Published by The X Press
6 Hoxton Square, London N1 6NU
Tel: 020 7729 1199
Fax: 020 7729 1771
Email: vibes@xpress.co.uk
www.xpress.co.uk

Printed by Omnia Books Ltd, Glasgow UK

For a free copy of this sampler contact The X Press on 020 7729 1199

ISBN 1-902934-14-8

Funded by
THE
ARTS
COUNCIL
OF ENGLAND

Brand Nu
was made possible by the involvement
of the following publishers:

Abacus
Angela Royale Press (ARP)
Black Amber Books
Bogle L'Ouverture
Crocus Books
Harlem River Press
Livewire
New Beacon Books
Pepal Tree Press
The Women's Press
The X Press

This book is
dedicated to the memory of
Clarissa Luard
who did so much to promote
the cause of literature.

With special thanks to John Hampson at the
Arts Council of England for all his tireless support
and encouragement.

INTRODUCTION

Welcome to *Brand Nu*, a unique sampler which was born out of the desire to highlight the rich diversity of current black writing. *Brand Nu* showcases some of the best black contemporary writing on the market across a range of independent presses. Sampling works from a diverse range of authors such as Diran Adebayo, Patrick Augustus, Leone Ross and Teddy Hayes, we hope that you will find this book inspiring reading.

Cross-Over is an introduction to *Brand Nu* written by a selection of journalists who share their thoughts on how the 'black experience' has affected both them and British society and on the 'quiet revolution' happening in the genre of black writing. The literary pundits say that black writing is coming out of the margins and reaching a wider mainstream audience. As we begin 2001 maybe this will be the year which will bring some noise to the 'quiet revolution.'

More and more people are buying in to, experiencing, or adopting cultures that are different to their own. Fashion, music, sport, the arts have led the way in creating a new indefinable global identity. Culture is moving away from being exclusive to one group, to being 'open to offers'.

Artists have always defied definition and black writers are no different. They might write from personal experiences, or record their own cultural environments,

1

but the stories they voice transcend all cultural barriers and touch everyone who has a heart or opinion. *Cross-Over* comments on how it feels to be on the outside and yet still embrace the culture from within.

After reading this sampler we would appreciate your comments. Email us on vibes@xpress.co.uk. Check out our web site on www. xpress.co.uk.

Jacqueline Asafu-Adjaye
Editor

CROSS-OVER

Dirk Robertson author of the crime thriller 'Highland T'ing', writes on his early experiences of black culture.

The year escapes me, but it was post 1977 as my flared trousers had been banished to a bin bag and I was living with Veronica, in The Meadows, a densely populated area of inner city Nottingham. A Scotsman who has spent his formative years in the precise but schizophrenic city of Edinburgh, mine has been an eventful journey of staggering contrasts, which continues to this day.

Veronica was one of three daughters of Mr and Mrs Blake who were from the parish of St. Catherine in Jamaica. The Caribbean must have seemed a long way off on those cold windswept northern nights. I'll never forget the Blakes, from whom I learnt many things which refuse to leave me.

That particular night Veronica took me to a performance by poet Linton Kwesi Johnson. I loved it. I was the only white guy in the audience and the rhythm of his voice and the strength of his passion touched me.

After the show, in the foyer three black men approached Veronica and I to commence a discussion around the fact that they felt that she, as a 'conscious' woman, should not be mixing with me, a white man. They talked, I listened. It was my first time touching on the subject but it was not to be my last.

Black people share common experiences but they do

3

not necessarily express themselves with one voice. This is true of the written word as it is of the spoken.

The years have fallen away now. Veronica lives in Jamaica, flared trousers are back and I've grown into something quite different to the awkward, insecure young man who rattled around in The Meadows.

I am thrilled to be contributing to the introduction of *Brand Nu*, which brings together a wonderful range of writing by new and established authors. The writings promote different styles with contrasting points, some pieces are gentle and sublime while others exclaim stinging acidity. But all the works espouse passion. Without that you have nothing.

Mike Best, Editor of 'The Voice' newspaper, refects on his early experiences of working within mainstream media.

I was humbled as I walked through the corridors of Broadcasting House for the first time in 1980. I was to become one of the few black journalists to join the production team of Radio 4's 'Today'-the flagship news programme.

My initial entry into the field of journalism came purely by chance. I have always had a burning interest in news and current affairs, but was oblivious to the fact that it would later become a significant factor in deciding my future. Being one of the first black producers on the 'Today' programme had its surprises. I once unwittingly recorded a voice-over package in the studio without seeking the assistance of a studio

4

assistant. On that occasion I was gently reminded that I was breaking the rules of the establishment by going it alone. But nothing prepared me for my second day of my attachment, as I relaxed in the corridor outside the production office. The BBC's Governor General who's office was only one floor above walked by and noddingly acknowledged my presence. But the tea lady was more curious than the Governor as to how I came to be loitering on the fourth floor.

"You must have lost your way. Are you looking for the restaurant my dear?" inquired the tea lady.

"What a strange question, I'm working on the 'Today' programme," I replied.

"I'm sorry, I thought you were looking for some of your friends who work in the restaurant with me," she said.

On a brighter note, 'Today' was an exciting and interesting experience, so too was the stint at Broadcasting Unit at Westminster. There were no formal introductions at either offices, one had to be a self starter and the term 'being thrown in at the deep end,' became a reality.

I will always be eternally grateful to the late Brian Redhead, one of the programme's most popular presenters for 'showing me the ropes'. His gentleness and wit transcends the tough image with which he was portrayed during interviews.

My career as head of news and current affairs at Sunset Radio, Britain's second black-run commercial radio station was an equally challenging prospect. Its demise serves as a stark reminder of the deep gulf between those who own and control the wealth behind such enterprises.

Former 'New Nation' News Editor Ross Slater, shares his thoughts on the cross-cultural appeal of black writing from a media perspective.

When I first went to work for Hansib Publishing, who were the owners of the 'Caribbean Times' and 'Asian Times' in those days, my intention was to become a sports reporter. The West Indian cricket team were touring and I thought that I could re-integrate myself with journalism following a three year degree and catch some rays at the same time. I was in for a big disappointment.

The 'Caribbean Times' and 'Asian Times might not have much of a staff between them but they did have a sports reporter who kept a tight grip on his cricket patch.

They told me I could write news stories for the papers. I argued that my ignorance of Asian culture in particular should rule me out but they wouldn't hear of it and that is how I started.

Having spent a year working as a staff reporter for the 'News of The World', the black press was a serious culture shock. There were no long lunch breaks, no expenses forms to fill in, no editor on your case and no-one jumped to attention when you told them where you were phoning from. Nobody rang you up asking for money for a story (if they had you would have laughed at them) and unlike at the 'News of The World', where only a fraction of what was written went into the paper, these black papers never said 'no' if there was a space to fill.

Things have improved. The 'New Nation' and 'Caribbean Times' today are infinitely more professional than they were in the past and they are certainly more popular with the readers. In the old days (and by this I mean five years ago) you would write story after story but you'd never know if anyone had read the paper because feedback would be zero.

I think this was because the stories were so much about race and injustice that readers, quite sensibly, couldn't be bothered to add their outrage.

Now, with the national press writing more about racial injustice than ever before, there is no longer the over-riding pressure on a black newspaper to report every injustice. Newspapers like books, are a part of peoples, leisure time so they want to see their inner thoughts, prejudices and lives reflected, as well as feeling that they are a little better informed than when they started. As a white man who worked almost by accident on a black newspaper the experience has been an education for me.

With increasing numbers of British families being racially mixed, black literature and newspapers serve increasingly as a gateway to a little bit of knowledge for white people who want to know more. I know that white people read 'New Nation' as well as black books and that's great. And why not? For centuries, black people have been reading European based literature and newspapers and have become experts on white people as a consequence. Now the worm is turning just a little and promotions such as *Brand Nu* are in the vanguard of that process.

Newspaper columnist Yasmin Alibhai-Brown, speaks on how she deals with being an Asian woman working within mainstream media.

I came to this country in 1972 from Uganda. Since the day I arrived here, I have wanted to have some influence over the ways ideas are generated and how these change society. I feel a mixture of gratitude (to the gods) and of fury (against those who run the media) that I am, as far as I know, the only black/Asian woman who has a regular column on a national newspaper in this country. It has been a hard slog. I wish I had chosen to be a millionaire instead. But this is what I dreamt about and this is what I do now. Why does it matter? Because in a Western democracy the comment pages of a newspaper have more power than can be imagined. I have had ministers, consultants, heads of police forces, BBC managers, directors of other organisations all reporting (often defensively) to what I write.

And what I say is different because it challenges their presumptions about policies, ideas, judgements. For example when I wrote to say that Italian food in this country is over-rated and has much to do with Europeans needing to eat comfort food, fat-cat chefs in this country boiled over with rage. I said that New Labour was not serious about racial equality because it kept out black Britons from places where real power is exerted. Four ministers rose to defend the record. What I also do is cast a critical eye over our communities. This can be the hardest thing to do because racism has made people from ethnic minority communities reluctant to look at their own responsibilities.

As an Asian woman I do question the sexist assumptions which are rife in both the black and Asian communities. But always, when you are in this position you know, in your bones, that you owe it to your people never to betray them and make their lives worse than they were before you got that spot on the newspaper.

Paul Bradshaw Editor of the urban jazz magazine 'Straight No Chaser' says that he owes his inspiration for this piece to Teddy Hayes' novel 'Blood Red Blues', which conjured up musical memories of Curtis Mayfield. Paul describes the breaking out of jazz, soul and hip hop music from the ghetto and how it effectively blasted its way into the suburbs of white America. He makes striking comparisons between black writers and music stars, drawing on their propensity to take hold of the soul.

I have a vivid recollection of a meeting with the poet Jayne Cortez. Once married to avant garde saxophonist Ornette Coleman and leader of her own band the Firespitters, she recalled enthusiastically how the rhythmic wave of resistance that unfurled during the sixties in the States generated a new generation of do-it-yourself publishers who gave voice to a new generation of African-American and Hispanic writers and poets. That voice corresponded to the relentless pursuit of progress in the music whether in the shape of the underground- the jazz that tuned to the Freedom Principal- or the R&B that was constantly reshaping the contemporary 'pop' agenda. Just as with the major record companies, the big publishing companies recognised new talent and new markets and the artistic endeavours of writers like Alice Walker and Toni Morrison made them 'stars' in the same way that Stevie Wonder, Marvin Gaye or Miles Davis were. It's difficult to measure progress but in these times we still need those innovative indie publishers whose roots in the community allow writers, young and old, to take flight on the wings of a strong cultural identity. Just as in the music we need people to give us a little magic, to tap into the spirit and engage in, and crossover into an arena where cultural differences are becoming blurred and falling by the wayside. To paraphrase one Twentieth Century genius, Duke Ellington: "There's two kinds of music. Good music and bad music."

Bobby Ayyub Syed founder and Director of the Ethnic Multi Cultural Media Awards (EMMA), shares his thoughts on race.

The ever powerful British media industry has not always recognised the positive images of this truly unique ethnic multicultural community, this diversity makes many of us feel extremely proud to be British, within a country that has a great economic and cultural history. This vast city of London has 33 different ethnically based communities with numbers exceeding 100,000 as well as 300 different languages spoken within this unique metropolitan environment.

The 'Life Time Achievement Award' bestowed upon Muhammad Ali during the June 99 EMMA Awards was a forerunner for the national recognition he received by the British public black and white alike, for Sports Personality of the Century. The sports, music and art industries have managed to break through racial boundaries by creating pop or sport icons who are defined by their success or infectious star qualities rather than by their race.

Britain has a distinct integrated outlook for the younger ethnic multicultural generations. The Stephen Lawrence Inquiry unmasked the racial divide that still exists within certain pockets of British society. Stephen Lawrence's death announced the fear that every non-white person still faces potential persecution against the colour of one's skin.

EMMA to a large extent is a personal journal of discovery amidst a society based upon racial harmony and opportunity for all, regardless of race, creed or colour. My father had migrated to London in the early 60's from Pakistan to work and support his family, once invited to do so by the then British government, and worked extremely hard without holidays to support a large extended family. The stories regarding this period of migration have touched every Commonwealth citizen, who looked forward to a better way of life, in the same way as the Irish who migrated to America, in search of prosperity and freedom.

The EMMA 2000 lifetime achievement award went to Mr Nelson Mandela and on receiving the award he spoke on his initial reflections on the eve of the New Millennium, his words struck a chord and encapsulated my 'tomorrow vision'. Nelson Mandela said that he wished, "that the people of the world would find a way to live in peace, not to forget the past, but to reconcile all the aspects of history and turn it into an experience on how to deal with conflict, reconciliation and how to live peacefully with one's neighbour regardless of the past and the damage it may have done."

―――――――――――――――――――――――――――――

Promised Land
DOTUN ADEBAYO

Dotun Adebayo, former Music Editor for the 'Voice' newspaper, is a columnist for both 'Pride' magazine and the 'New Nation' newspaper. As well as freelancing for the 'Guardian' and other national newspapers, he hosts his own book show, on BBC 'London Live' radio station.

He is the author of the satirical book entitled, 'Can I have My Balls Back Please? Targeted, he says, at the "so called 'new man', and all those men out there who have lost their balls to their girlfriends, wives, partners, mistresses, and who have suffered thirty years of gradual castration since Germaine Greer's feminist bible - 'The Female Eunuch'."

He has just completed 'Promised Land' and on catching a glimpse of the pre-pressed manuscript it is rather hard to believe that this is his debut novel. Narrated in cinematic epic tones, it tells the story of three generations of the Oswald family as they try to clutch to their piece of the promised land.

Adebayo's style is quintessentially bold and uncompromising. Written in primary colours, he challenges the reader not to react to the reel of events that take place.

As a new novelist it is difficult to pin him down as we watch him transcend in any given literary genre.

Angel Wright
Freelance Journalist & Literary Critic

ACT 1

The night the ninth earl was born, the heavens lapsed into an old fashioned hellfire-and-damnation frenzy. The moon was copper-coloured and the sky was black. Hailstones the size of three penny bits tumbled hard, the stars refused to shine and clouds twisted furiously as the possessed and tormented wind blew its way through town and country, uprooting fences, trees and telegraph poles in the path of its fearsome rage. Forked lightning cleaved the air and the earth shook, mighty mountains trembled and rivers ran upstream for hundreds of miles. In the angry howl, the hum of a mournful and desperate lament died away in the night.

Misery! Oh, misfortune!

A long, unbroken wail, no longer an undercurrent but a heavy and pulsating roar. The messenger of doom rode in with the night and galloped apace through the storm-battered gates of Elgin House, proclaiming the Glory of God. Erected in ancient stone to divine specifications and embellished inside and out with gold and silver, this magnificent stately home was the birthplace to generation after generation of power, pride and privilege where century after century, anointed blood ruled over lush acres stretching out into sleepy meadows, enchanting woods, eerie lakes and rolling hills in every direction far beyond the vision of the naked eye.

In the candle-lit shadows of its great hall, the tall silhouette of an aging duchess cursed like the devil before a church full of sinners as she dragged a woman less than half her age, like a dog along the oak-tiled floor.

Villain! Whore! Jezebel!

Like any old washer woman. No beauty in her voice nor graciousness or eloquence in her speech. No dignity of rank. Oh what wickedness! This was no random rage, but cool, calculated and reasoned.

Vanity, vanity, all is vanity.

Cry mercy for the dearly beloved. Mercy for the blessed and for the sanctified.

Mercy for the cursed and the despised, and for the cast aside child who, death staring her in the face moments before, had with one final painful push, brought her first born into the world wailing in a low moan. *"Oh Mary, Mother of God, Mother of Mercy,"* crying in a loud groan. *"Mary Apolita, Mother of mothers, Mother of Grace,"* in a soft sob. *"I swear by the Gospel and all the angels and saints of heaven, I have done you no wrong..."*

In the nearby chapel where ancestral bones have lain interned for a hundred thousand eerie nights, the sound of the great bell cut through the howl of the storm, announcing the birth of a son and heir while blow after blow rained down about the younger woman's head. Blood trickled from her nose as a vicious kick slammed into her face.

"Come quickly death, for I have need of you," she prayed.

But it was too late for prayers. High above her head, the gold panelled walls and the sparkling chandeliers, she thought she saw an angel fly across the canvas of the vast ceiling on which a biblical scene had been painted by some long forgotten artist from another age.

15

Its centrepiece was a magnificent family crest emblazoned with its ancient motto: *Blood is everything*.

Life, not death, replied. The tiniest of heads squeezed its way out from between her legs, kicking like the devil, fingers reaching restlessly and hungrily for the nipple at the mother's breast. Unlike his twin, this baby was born white.

ACT 2

Death, the mosquito, poised to suck the nectar of life where he can, revisited Lucky Valley that night, blowing his toxic fragrance amongst the ancestral spirits which nightly come with lightning bugs and buzzing crickets in search of food that superstitious souls leave out for them. A drum pan sound exploded into the sultry midnight air echoing beyond the hills and down in the valleys. Boom. BOOM. Boom. A loud, slow and solemn beat, followed by a short beat, a pause, then that long beat again. This could mean one thing, to the valley people knew, somebody had died. From settlement to settlement they loudly beat the same mournful rhythm.

Boom. BOOM. Boom. A drum beat potent enough to revive the recently departed. From somewhere in the hills, haunting voices joined in repeatedly raising the most heart rending wail - perhaps a secular, perhaps a spiritual, perhaps a hymn - starting with one voice and then one by one more and more until a chorus of scores had lifted their voices to the heavens. Somewhere in the valley a baby cried and a mother called out for her child in the dark night.

A cacophony of sounds screamed through the night

air as goats, sheep, fowl and stray pigs brayed, bleated, clucked and squealed with a rooster cockadoodledoing at their impending doom. A feast would be laid for the living and the dead. There would be plenty to eat.

Behind a low mud wall, against the background of a moonlit sky, dark silhouettes washed their hands and feet and faces quietly in an ancient custom before entering the home of the bereaved. In keeping with tradition, the deceased's hat hung above the entrance.

Inside the crowded two-roomed clay hut, a wrinkled old black woman, but recently stolen away to Jesus, lay silent and motionless on her death bed, as a youth with a strong angular negro face measured her up with a string.

Queenie was washed then adorned. They had smeared on her fat roasted pig, then dressed and scented her. They had rubbed red ocher on her skin and whitened her teeth with ash until they were the colour of milk. They had placed heavy pennies on their dearly departed's eyes and had sprinkled salt on Queenie's stomach to keep the evil spirits away. Then one by one they paid their respects by placing their hands on her cold forehead for good luck and whispering softly in her ear, saluting her with personal goodbyes.

"Honour an' Glory Miss Queenie, Honour an' Glory to, you."

"Me conscience a-bite me. I wish we could go back to we humble peacefulness."

"Praises be, me glad fi know dat you reach paradise."

"Go in peace. It is God who calls you."

"A day will come when we shall meet again."

"Don't call me, 'cause I'm not ready to go with you yet."

"Live long, live long, live long."

"Between me and you is only the light of the day."

They formed a half circle around Queenie, a prayer was said, followed by more singing. Some wailed and moaned, some ushered silent tears of sorrow with fears of the years until they met again at the pearly gates. Junior would keep vigil through the night.

Proper respect to the departed required that the body not be left unattended until burial. His long face drawn further, he stared down at Miss Queenie's peaceful dead face and tried to remember the good times and the blessings she had showered on Lucky Valley. She had lived to a good old age, yet no one could quite believe that Queenie was gone, dead. *Who was going to take her place?*

The drumming had continued throughout the night. Those same drums which had once called their foreparents to steal away from slavery.

A cock crowed and the drumming stopped abruptly. In its place a long note trumpeted through a cowrie shell. It was finally time and from all around, people came through the night to join the funeral procession.

Queenie's lifeless body had been lifted into an oversized coffin and carried out to the place of burial by the mysterious spring whose waters cured many ailments which physicians had previously pronounced incurable.

"Goin to see Jesus in the moring
I ain't got long to stay.
Tell old Pharaoh,
let my people go!
No more shall they in bondage toil."

As they have done for hundreds of years, the people of Lucky Valley saluted the dearly departed in the loudest way they could. Clapping, whirling and whooping, they accompanied the coffin along the torchlit route the few hundred yards to the burial ground, where Bro' Uriah, the designated preacher, waited with his head bowed solemnly.

"Brothers and sisters," he boomed when the procession was settled, *"brothers and sisters, we are gathered here today to bid farewell to our beloved sister, Miss Queenie and to ask the Lord to shower her with goodness and mercy."*

"Brothers and sisters, weep, weep, a good woman has left us. She lived amongst us, but now she is dead. Her father lived amongst us, he is dead. Her mother lived amongst us, she is dead. But her good works is still amongst us. We weep to console ourselves because of her good works."

Somebody wailed out loud.

"Lord save our sister's soul, be with her." A loud cry of *"amen"*, followed by a deathly hush as the coffin was lowered into the grave.

In death, it is not his deserts that a man gets but his destiny. Queenie was sent back from the other side like a cat with nine lives.

The tap-tap-tapping sent a chill through those at the graveside, but it took them a few moments to realise that it was coming from within the wooden box now laid to rest, but no sooner had it become clear, than their faces ashened and their eyes widened and they couldn't get out of that burial ground fast enough, their shirt-backs full of wind.

Orange Laughter
LEONE ROSS

Leone Ross delivers an inspiration in 'Orange Laughter' with all the uncompromise of an artist totally absorbed in her art. Her work has a style which is abstract, sublime and experimental. Her debut novel 'All the Blood is Red' was listed for the Orange Prize. In the case of 'Orange Laughter' if a literary equivalent to the Turner Prize existed then undoubtedly 'Orange Laughter' would be on its shortlist.

The novel revisits the haunts of racial conflict and identity politics through the refreshing simple narrative of it's two young male protagonists, Tony a young black boy and his white friend Mikey, who is bullied because of his weight.

In an interview in 'Calabash' magazine by Omega Douglas, Ross is questioned over her omission of punctuation in the opening chapter, simply called 'Tony'.

"Whenever I started writing him he refused punctuation," said Ross who went on to explain that her characters always come to her and speak to her. Mikey first appeared to her whilst studying at Kingston University. He introduced himself to her as a fat, little white boy from a small town in America's deep south, who had a beautiful black boy for a best friend who looked out for him.

The style adopted for Tony's narrative provides a portal for the reader who enters his nightmarish existence, surviving amongst the rats under New York's subway, living in blackness, destitute and incognito.

We walk, stumble and run the length and breadth of Tony's bleak mental terrain, rays of relief break through only when Ross freezes his narrative which takes place in contemporary New York and takes us back to North Carolina, set in the midst of 1960's Civil Rights political unrest. Tony seeks refuge in his childhood memories where he finds laughter and feels safe and loved.

On her writing, Leone seems reticent, *"I'd say to my mentor, I can't write like Toni Morrison, I'm crap,' and he'd say, 'but you will write like Leone Ross and that will be quite fine."*

Jacqueline Asafu Adjaye

TONY

I haven't been Topside and watched the breeze for over a year, but I went out the other night after the little boy lay dead in my arms I had to mail an important letter and there was wax on my fingers which dripped from the angry candle it made hot white circles on my skin, pattering one two, one two, burn baby burn, I need a candle because it's dark down here. The dark is thick like oatmeal, like nothing you've ever seen and I can hear a train in the distance sometimes it freaks me out big time, because you feel like it's coming to get you even when you know it's not scheduled. Baby, you know down here we all dream that the trains will get us and run us over, or the third rail will fry us one strange night when the balance goes, when you're stepping over the tracks, you know what I mean about the third rail. Right, the rail that they run those million watts through. That's right, Chaz is always saying that one day she's going to drop kick it like a stupid motherfucker and deep fry herself on that rail. YOU CAN RING MY BE-E-ELL, RINGIN MY BELL, MY BELL, DING DONG DING OW.

I was writing the letter under the candle with the wax on my fingers and I wanted to ask Chaz to mail it for me. When she goes Topside, she goes to pan-handle, but she's a jealous bitch too. Why am I surrounded by all these bitches? So I made a decision that I had to do it myself and I ran my thumbs over the letter that I'd written and thought about Chaz telling me how she gets her letters from her sister who thinks that her fine ass self is working as a dancer. But really she's living underneath here with me. Chaz said, *'yeah Tony you could get post at the gas station. They good like that, there's a fine brother across the counter and he gives me free Hershey's and those cigarettes you smoking.'* All I know is she wanted me to cop an attitude because she called the brother *fine* but I don't give a good goddamn I like Chaz and the pussy is good but I can't love in a place like this.

Jealousy is for Topside. It's for real life, for 42nd street, McDonald's, Queens, the Statue of Liberty. Whenever I tell Chaz about the Lady, she asks me,I tell her she's just a cynic, because this is the land of the free and the home of the brave. She thinks I'm serious. You could never say that Chaz had an ear for irony or sarcasm.

I knew Chaz would ask too many questions if I asked her to mail the letter, so I took the few short paces up the ladder, yeah, up to Topside. I wanted to fall when the night hit me. It wasn't dark enough and the moon was so bright I hadn't seen it for a year and the silver shadows were merry. Goddamn, I still got a turn of phrase and I crushed the envelope in my hand. I kept saying this is the only way a man has to admit that he needs some help. Not a lot of help, just a little. You know, a man needs to ask a friend for a favour sometimes and the moon laughed down at me. The letter is going to Doctor Michael Abraham Tennyson. When he gets it we could have a great reunion, yeah, class of North Carolina 1965. He could remind me that she's DEAD. Agatha's dead.

I know she's dead, but I need him to tell me the whole story of how we came to be best buds. I know she's dead but I saw her yesterday and I know you think I'm crazy but her face was so sweet. I swear when she laughs, it's orange and there are yellow pools at her feet and her arms are red with blood, so I wrote him.

Now I'm sitting Underneath in the subway tunnels, where I live. Nobody knows I'm here. I'm waiting because Mikey was the best friend a man ever had. I know he's going to come through for me. It's a damn shame we haven't spoken so long. How old were we, twelve, thirteen, nine when we first met ? I've written him and told him I can't get the Soul Snatcher out of my mind.

Edene, North Carolina

The black boy picked pecans every day at nine o' clock. Mikey started worming his way under Miss Ezekiel's house at 8:30. His bulk made the venture difficult, but he'd mastered the art, pulling his stomach towards his backbone and crushing the small breasts on his chest

23

against the rough dirt. The best way was to lie on his prize winning stomach, sweat turning his shirt dark, shuffling backwards. Once he'd wedged his legs and hips as far as they could go, he braced himself on his hands and pushed backwards against the ground. Inch by inch, his body complied. When he was in position only his fingers showed, and he was trapped until the black boy left. Getting out was harder.

Each time he hid under the house, Mikey spent a few minutes in prayer. He prayed that Miss Ezekiel would never see him struggling. From where he lay he could feel movement inside the building: Miss Ezekiel and Agatha walking in the kitchen, frying meat and making biscuits. Agatha stepping through, sweeping the floors. In his most horrific imaginings he could see the moment his grandmother spotted the big moving lump that was him, bending the floorboards. She would call Agatha and she'd say, *'What in all hell is that? Agatha, come over heah, watch out fo' snakes and jes' you see what's the cause of this heah hump.'* Then they would find him, stuck, dirty, too slow and too big to scramble out. The black boy would turn around and finally speak to him, and the words would be damning: *'Whatchoo doin' watchin' me?'*. It would all be out and he would have to raise his eyes to heaven and die. Mikey blinked as sweat trickled into his left eye and sighed as the back door opened. He heard the boy's soft foot fall on the front steps.

Miss Ezekiel told him that you could smell niggers before they came up on you, if the wind was blowing right. She said she was surprised people didn't just lay down and die when all of them got together. That was probably why intelligent folks didn't encourage them to gather. She said, when she passed them nigger gin joints in town, she smelled them on the air. All drink and sinning. She said she was surprised that these silver-rights goings on didn't kill the police with the stench. Mikey had never smelt anything special on the niggers. Just sweat and a Sunday afternoon, like him. Except Agatha.

Mikey smiled, thinking about her. Agatha, Miss Ezekiel's daily help, who came six days a week, at seven in the morning. Agatha, who smelled good every day. Even when the heat blistered the porch walls, and a man could drink shade like lemonade, she smelled good. He shifted, thinking about her and the way she made ice cream, cranking the old machine. One day her sweat had dripped onto his arm as she handed him a bowl. It was all the best smells in the world. Her skin was like hot butter in a pan. He could imagine her pouring herself over biscuits.

He'd been in Edene for eighteen months, since Miss Ezekiel brought him over from his home town in Georgia. Two days after they arrived, Agatha came to the back door, looking for work. Mikey watched the tall, brown-skinned woman duck her way into the house and then looked away. He was more concerned with his own lingering disorientation. It had only been four months since his father had died, and he didn't like his Miss Ezekiel. The house his grandmother had rented - with his father's money, he was sure - still looked unknown and empty, despite the boxes and bags strewn in the front room and across the porch. Miss Ezekiel hadn't let him bring anything that belonged to him. She bought him all new clothes. She said all of his daddy's things smelled like death.

In Georgia, the people on the street had

respected his daddy too much to exclaim about his fat son. But in Edene, each new person he met widened their eyes, as if they were trying to accommodate his body. He watched them pity him. Mrs Jenkins - Miss Ezekiel's neighbour, who had her up in all the sewing circles, all the church meetings - took one look at him and proclaimed him as wide as he was tall. She said it in a loud voice. Mikey dipped his head and scurried inside himself. That was where he lived.

Agatha was different. When she saw him, her eyes had widened too, but there was something warm there. She looked at him thoughtfully, as if she'd been about to say something but changed her mind. When Miss Ezekiel turned away, Agatha put out one hand and stroked the damp hair off his forehead. She wrinkled her nose at Miss Ezekiel's back, a conspiratorial gesture that made him smile.

Agatha was six feet tall if she was a mile, and her hair wasn't like any colour Mikey had seen before. It fell from a widow's peak into slender black ropes, past the bright cloth in her hair and down across her shoulders. When she held her head just so, secret strands went blue. Her skin was high yellow-brown and her feet were small. When you got up close, your eyes were drawn to a surprise in her face: thin lines crawled across her right cheekbone, around the eye socket, scattered across half of her forehead, crept under her chin and down her neck. She watched him looking and smiled, as if to say yes, I see you looking, I see you've seen it, now what? He blushed and moved away. On that ice cream day he sat down with his dried, sweated-on arm, smelling her, until Miss Ezekiel called him, fussing, asking him what the hell he was doing. He'd sniffed the Agatha-smell all day. It was the smell of love.

Four months ago, as July's weight bent down upon them like an old man with a burning ambition, Agatha had introduced the black boy. His name was Tony. She came to the back door holding his hand. Mikey climbed out of his room to look at him. He wanted to hate him: Tony was as beautiful as a girl. Mikey was awed, looking at the boy's bowed head. The sunshine made Tony's skin glossy. He had a new haircut. Agatha explained that when Tony arrived at the bus station from New York, his head was all rat tails. She couldn't untangle it, so she sheared it off.

Tony looked up at her as she spoke. He was pretty, but he was going to be a man. Thick eyelashes framed his bottomless eyes. Blackberry eyes. He looked at Mikey looking at him while Agatha explained chores: Miss Ezekiel wanted the lawn cut and she wanted the silver cleaned and boy, we've got to move on now. Her voice was firm and peaceful.

Tony didn't speak. He nodded to show that he understood. Agatha said he never uttered a word. Mikey wondered if the black boy was a retard. He knew that Miss Ezekiel didn't like the lack of yessum, no-um. He'd realised early, that words like that made his grandmother happy. But there was nothing Miss Ezekiel could change about the silent boy in her house all summer. Mikey listened to her comfort herself out loud, in the evenings as he did his homework at the dinner table, knees together, hands flat on the table top like he was told, doodling around the edge of the paper when he couldn't get the work right: the boy was clean, Agatha was a decent coloured and the Lord, well He did send things to test a body.

Mikey avoided Tony, as he avoided most.

When the school holidays had started, he'd found once more that he had no friends, and needed no more enemies. There wasn't much to do except go into the woods, avoiding the swamp, lest Miss Ezekiel start hollering, his niggershooter in one hand and food in a bag: quarter of a watermelon, some biscuits, a handful of peanuts and one of Miss Ezekiel's chickens fried up brown and smelling good, in case he needed to keep his strength up. He tried fishing in the creek, but the fish just seemed to laugh up at him, and he was tired of that, so he kept walking, looking at squirrels and shooting at them. He knew he'd miss but it didn't bother him. He liked squirrels. It was just that he couldn't take any joy in the summer, like a nine year old boy should. He wasn't good at anything and eventually when the sun became merciless, he decided to go home. It was like this every day, and before he knew it, school was in again and the teasing began again and this, he decided, was his life. Yells of disgust in the hallways and no-one ever talking to him without contempt. Until October came, and the pecans began to fall. It had been another long day when he happened upon Tony in the yard, picking pecans, and talking.

Mikey wriggled, trying to get comfortable as Tony walked forward into his range. He grinned to himself, then frowned. It would soon be over. The pecans were only good for a couple more days. When Tony had started picking, they were nearly three inches thick on the ground. Miss Ezekiel was mighty proud of the pecan trees on her new land. Tony shook out the first sack and began to pick up nuts. When he first heard the black boy's voice, Mikey was too shocked to make out the words. He'd paused, excited, debating the wisdom of running out and saying hey, or running into the house and telling Agatha, to let her praise the Lord for a miracle. He would have given his whole lunch and a lot more to be responsible for a light in her face. He moved behind a tree and listened, his stomach churning. It was only a murmur, but the words were unmistakable.

'*An' Elimelech, Naomi's husband died, an' she was left, an' her two sons....*' said Tony.

Mikey guessed that it was the Bible. He wondered whether it was such a good idea to run inside and tell Agatha. If the boy was talking damnation maybe that would make her sad. He leaned against the tree and listened. His daddy once told him he had good ears.

'*An' they took them wives of the women of Moab, an' the name of the one was Orpah, an' the name of the other Ruth, an' they dwelled there about ten years...*' said Tony, picking up pecans.

Mikey had seen the coloured all hollering and shouting up in their churches. Agatha's grandaddy had been a preacher. Maybe she knew. Maybe she'd been teaching Tony the Bible. Maybe it was the only thing he could say. He listened to the pleasant voice and decided that he liked it. It was soothing. His daddy's voice had been good too: cutting through noise like water. Mikey crouched behind the tree for a long time, hearing about Ruth's life, until Agatha called for Tony and the boy went inside.

For three days Mikey hid under the house, waiting to hear Tony speak. He didn't know why he was doing it. He only knew that it distanced the self-consciousness in his belly. It was their secret, even if Tony didn't know Agatha was tearing out her hair about why this boy don't speak, but he, Mikey, could see Tony doing it every day. Words running out of his mouth into the combustible afternoons. It was like watching a miracle. He thrilled to himself when he saw Miss Ezekiel muttering under her breath, cussing how this little nigger better not be sassing her with his buttoned-up lip. He knew that Tony was more than silence. Mikey smiled as Tony took a breath and began.

'The song of songs, which is Solomon's. Let him kiss me with the kisses of his mouth, for their love is better than wine...'

It was a good secret for a little boy who couldn't hit the house with a rock if he tried. A boy who had comics on his shelf, until Miss Ezekiel found them and burned them. Watching Superman and Spiderman go up in flames, he wanted Spidey to jump out of that big old fire and give Miss Ezekiel a hiding. Then they would be friends, he and Spidey, go up North on Greyhound and no-one would think he was a sissy boy then. Spidey would teach him how to use his Spidey sense and he'd know who was a bad 'un and he would leave all them bad folks alone.

'I am black, but comely, o ye daughters of Jerusalem, as the tents of Kedar, as the curtains of Solomon. Look not upon me, because I am black, because the sun hath looked upon me...'
Tony said.

When Spiderman declined the offer and continued to burn, Mikey wasn't surprised. Nothing good had happened to him since his daddy died. He saw Agatha shaking her head. Later she asked Miss Ezekiel in that fancy voice of hers - better, Mikey admitted than his grandmother's or his own - why Miss Ezekiel felt the need to be burning up the boy's only pleasure. Miss Ezekiel turned her back on Agatha and there was nothing more to be said. He noticed that Miss Ezekiel didn't give Agatha any of the leftover clabber milk that evening. Agatha's fancy voice fascinated him almost as much as her face. Almost as much as Tony's incorporeal murmur.

'I have compared thee, o my love, to a company of horses in Pharoah's chariots. Thy cheeks are comely with rows of jewels, thy neck with chains of gold...' said Tony.

Mikey strained to hear, hoping snakes wouldn't eat his knees.

'We will make thee borders of gold with studs of silver. Thy lips, o my spouse, drop as the honeycomb, honey and milk are under thy tongue and the smell of thy garments....'

'Michael Abraham! Michael Abraham? Where is that boy?'

Mikey banged his head against the floorboards above him. It hurt so much that he bit his bottom lip to restrain a yelp. Bruised air exploded from his lungs in a sharp hiss. Miss Ezekiel was yelling from the house. He glanced back at Tony. He was still talking. Panic hit him. Surely Tony would hear her calling and shut his mouth. There must be a reason why Tony could talk and wasn't. There must be a very big reason.

'I said, Michael Abraham, where you at, boy?'

'Thy plants are an orchard of pomegranates, with pleasant fruits, camphire...' said Tony.

Mikey wished he would stop talking about campfires. His voice was getting louder. There would be hell to pay if Miss Ezekiel heard him. He was talking and talking, picking up pecans with his nimble fingers. They were nearly gone.

Mikey heard the sound of footsteps moving

through the house above him. Miss Ezekiel was heading for the back door. They'd both get a whipping. Miss Ezekiel would know that Tony had been fooling her. She'd know that he, Mikey, had been listening. She might say it was a plan that Agatha knew all along. She might tell her to get going. The thought made him bite his lip even harder. And Tony was still talking, as if he couldn't stop.

Miss Ezekiel would be opening the back door soon. She was shouting at the top of her voice. Why couldn't Tony hear?

'Michael? I said, Michael, where are you, boy?'

Maybe this was a punishment. He was going to be found out, lying and watching a nigger talk out the Lord's words, like he was somebody. Like he was black and comely like Solomon said. He'd asked his teacher what comely meant and she said it was another word for pretty. Miss Ezekiel was going to find out and Tony was going on and on, as if he was in a trance, squeezing the plump nuts in his small fists, dropping them in yet another sack, using his enchanted, pained voice. He had to distract her. He could hear her on the steps.

'Mizz Ezekiel! Mizz Ezekiel!' Mikey yelled.

Tony jumped like the devil was coming and peered over the sack in his hand. He looked alarmed, furtive, embarrassed and angry all at the same time.

Miss Ezekiel's voice sounded even more annoyed. Mikey scrabbled at the ground in front of him, hoisting his weight forward. He had to get to his feet. Miss Ezekiel was coming down the steps and around the house. He could see her long feet and cracked toes in the sandals she wore. He gripped at the ground. His nails scraped against stones that cut into his palms. She was going the wrong way, heading around the left hand side of the house, peeping, arthritis making her joints rustle. Any moment now she was going to be standing over him, yelling out that he should be afraid of snakes and ha'ants under the house, how you put yo' fat self up under that porch anyhow, boy, is you a fool? A panicked tear squeezed itself out of his eye as he tried to lever his feet into a position from which he could push. He was stuck.

A pair of brown legs appeared in front of him. A brown hand reached out. Mikey gaped up in astonishment as Tony grasped his hand and pulled. He felt as if his gut would rip. A nipple scraped against splinters. Tony braced himself and pulled again. Mikey felt himself sliding. Tony flailed and lost his balance and the two boys fell to the ground, Mikey almost in Tony's arms. They could hear Miss Ezekiel's patterned footfall coming back around - *'Boy, where you at, looka heah, don' be playin' with me now!'* - and Tony tugged again. Then they were both on their feet, panting. Tony's face was solemn. Miss Ezekiel turned the corner of the house just as Agatha came to the front steps.

'Tony! Why you not pickin' those pecans? Get on, now!' she said. Her hand clenched and unclenched her skirt.

Miss Ezekiel stared at Mikey's shirt. Dust painted the front and a rip hung sadly on the sleeve.

'Boy, you a fool? I need you ta be inside these books! What you out heah doin'? What you do to yo' shirt?'

Mikey looked down. Out of the corner of his eye he saw Tony hurrying back to the nuts, picking faster than ever.

'Nothin', ma'am,' he said.

'Then get in the house, boy!'

He smiled up the steps. He looked at Tony but

the boy had his head down again. Mikey decided that he didn't care. Now they shared the secret.

It was out in the open and he didn't care about the fussing. Everything was fine.

Colin Channer is the author of the celebrated 'Waiting In Vain' (Ballantine, 1997) and 'Natural Mystic' (Ballantine, 1998). His screenplay 'Natural Mystic' is currently in contract stages with Island Films Jamaica. He is a trained journalist and TV producer.

Born in Jamaica in 1963 Channer is very much a Kingston boy who can't believe all this is happening to him. He still plays soccer with his friends on a Sunday morning and fantasises about being the bass in a reggae band.

He is the Editor of 'Wheel & Come Again' an anthology of reggae inspired poems. *Brand Nu* samples the work of Vejay Steede from this much sought after collection. Vejay is an up-and-coming Bermudan poet, although he sees himself as 'nation-less' his work is heavily influenced by West Indian culture, and the likes of Marcus Garvey, Bob Marley and Kamau Braithwaite. He says that he aims to create a space where 'Blakkness may be celebrated without fear or shame.' Reggae is his first published poem.

Colin Channer writes a few words on 'Wheel & Come Again'.

Wheel is Caribbean poetry it's a real boomshot tribute to reggae music. Ambitious in scope and impressive in execution, 'Wheel & Come Again' is more than a collection of clear-eyed writing. It's a gun salute, a loud pram-pram, an echoing bawl of fah-wud supporting the idea that reggae is vital and valid as a literary model.

There is a lot to celebrate here. Seeing the work of newer writers such as the unfairly gifted Rohan Preston cotched against that of an enduring writer such as Olive, is reason enough to roll a spliff.

But can we call it an anthology? And should we even want to? That's a question we need to ask. Working like a selector on a heavyweight sound, cutting and mixing with experienced fingers, Dawes has created not an overview, not a survey, but something new and exciting that demands bolder definition. But what though? We're not sure yet. And that's part of the excitement. A great deal of it is textual, a fair expectation after a peep at the table of contents: James Berry, John Agard, Jean Breeze, Linton Kwesi Johnson, Fred D'Aguiar, Marc Matthews and Vejay Steede.

However a heap of it is textural, a point that becomes rachet sharp after penetrating this, that Dawes, without winking, nodding, or holding out his hand for a snare-slap high five, has found a way to blend into the mix, without breaking the groove.

The work of younger, less well-known poets, whose contribution in the 70s is in danger of being forgotten. Poets whose connection to the roots tradition, as either an influencer or practitioner, has to this point been overlooked.

That is the bigness of the collection. We still haven't found the right word yet it brings us the kind of fresh vision and expanded judgement more readily associated with a sip off a chalice filled to the brim with just-cut, slow-burning, green sensimilla, the kind we

Jamaicans keep a-yard when we send off de plane to farrin.

Reggae
By Vejay Steede

(Delroy Wilson on the CD player singing *I'm Still Waiting*)
Reggae is Afrika humming her favourite tune. Slaves singing as they cut cane in the heart of paradise. Reggae is Two Sevens clashing on the top of a hill. Blue mountains rolling. Calalloo. Chicken back.

Reggae is Roots Culture and Reality. A Concrete Jungle and a utopian vision all rolled into one. Down Ina de Ghetto.
Reggae is material privation and spiritual opulence.

Reggae is schizophrenic.
Reggae was born in Afrika and raised in Jamaica. It now lives in St. Ann.

Reggae is Rastaman chants over Nyabingi drums.
Reggae is Augustus Pablo's flute.
Reggae is Rita Marley getting High, So High. Ganja. Punny printas. Dancehall. Session.

Reggae is fast living and even faster fighting.

Reggae never dies a natural death.
War Ina Babylon. Reggae is Police and Thieves in the street Burning and Looting. RIOT. REVOLT. REVOLUTION!! Reggae is a posse of rude bwoys chanting down Babylon. Rasta philosophy. Selassie I know.

Reggae is Nanny, Cudjoe and Paul Bogle chasing Crazy Baldheads out of their yard. Leonard Howell preaching about a Blakk King. Alexander Bedward's Blakk wall.

Reggae is Blackness at its most beautiful. Shining, sparkling li. BLAKK LIFE. Black Uhuru screaming for Solidarity!! Reggae is Steve Biko and Winnie and Nelson Mandela.

Reggae is freedom rallying round the red, gold and green.

Reggae is Bob Marley.
Bob Marley is Reggae. Ziggy. Reggae is the Wailers wailing songs of freedom on a street corner in Kingston.

Reggae has a Black heart. Soul Fire. Marijuana brain. Pain. Reggae is struggle. CHAOS. CONFUSION. FIRE and BRIMSTONE burning down Babylon. Remembering Zion. Crying for Zion.
A-YAH-WE-DEH. A cultural rebellion.

Reggae is a Soul Rebel. Peter Tosh's version. Bunny Wailer wailing in Protest. Beres Puttin up a Resistance.

Reggae lives on the Front Line. Reggae is a Buffalo Soldier who never dies in battle. Reggae is IMMORTAL. Reggae never dies.

Healing Strategies for Women at War
FEMALE POETS

When we invited initial contributions we had no idea
what sort of anthology would result. Only that the
work of lesser known black women writers remain
largely unpublished by mainstream writers. Also, as
editors. we wanted to create an anthology of work
which reflected our experiences as women living
within a multiplicity of cultures. Here are seven women
writers, each writing with a distinct voice, whose
inspiration ranges from coats and photographs,
disfigured hearts and family relationships, to clifftop
love trysts and a woman's discourse with her own
body.

Brand Nu features the collection of Shamshad Khan and
Trudy Blake. Born in Leeds, Shamshad trained as a
biologist and later pursued her writing career in 1988.
Her poetry has been published in magazines and
anthologies including: 'The Fire People' (Payback
Press), 'Bitter Sweet' (Women's Press). Shamshad's
short story published by Virago, was later featured on
Radio 4's 'Love Thang'.

Trudy Blake immigrated from Jamaica and
arrived in England during the sixties. She worked as a
packer in Salford factories and as a sewing machinist
doing piecework. She now performs poetry across the
North West of England.

Jacqueline Roy, Senior Lecturer in Post- Colonial and
Creative Writing, Manchester Metropolitan University,

comments on the experiences gathered in 'Healing Strategies'.

During the last ten years or more, new voices have been emerging: those of men and women of African or Asian descent who were either born in Britain or came here as young children in the fifties, sixties and seventies.

The acknowledgement of these poets, novelists and dramatists has been painfully slow; the media has consistently ignored Black British writers in favour of African-Americans. However, although many common themes are represented by those poets, each articulation is different and points to the richness of multi-culturalism that is now an aspect of British life. 'Healing Strategies' must be read by all those who have an interest in postcolonial, black British writings. It is hoped that it marks a period in which such writing is nurtured and given the recognition that it needs in order to flourish.

Poems by Shamshad Khan

<u>SPIDER WOMAN</u>

She spun the argument
with a thread
he could not follow

perfecting
the delicate construction

until he
 unsuspecting

fell
entangled

to
his

gentle destruction

UNDER THE ARCHES

Under the arches
of my feet

you rest your head
your oil shaved scalp
warm

so the curve
of your head
fits

grips
the part

of my feet
that never touch the ground.

<u>FIRSTSOUND</u>

Mother now i understand
the green clinical fear
of this land
fresh

and you held onto me
longer
than you needed

didn't release me

i must have sensed

turned my head away
feet first
appeared
when you agreed
we'd have to take it on

still
i wouldn't leave
your space
my place

so they pulled
forceps
and turned me
the first sound
i heard on my release
lying between your thighs

were your screams
and the second

His name (Allah-u-Akbhar)*

and your throbbing body wet
always untimely
the release.

*refers to the practice of reciting prayers in the ears of a new born
baby so the first sound it hears on entering the world is the name of
God.

SILVER THREADS

Together we built a palace
mahal
domes and minarets
tiny blue tiles and mirrors.

Wandered
hand in hand

warm feet
on cool floors.

Ran up stairs to call
from towers piercing skies.

Rushed through gardens
pomegranates and white flowers
ruby sweet pungent scent.

Trailed feet in fountained water
and when night fell
argued how many stars
embroidered the sky.

Sari like folds from the heavens
to drape us
liquid blue chiffon
and silver threads

we lay and unthreaded.
How rich we were
silver knots
untied piled high.

It was whilst i lay thus
stars in my hands
and the heavens on my lap

that you left.
i searched amongst the reams
of translucent hope
fearing at first that you had smothered

or like a baby
choked on a silver thing.

i searched our palaces for years.
Until
no longer ours
it became mine

all hope lost
single voice ringing
echoes returned
thrown from wall to wall.

i gathered our treasures and hide them in my purse

silver bits
spangled love

proof that i had not dreamed alone.

I WOULDN'T MIND A FREE TRIP HOME

Yesterday, I was trying to park my car, except
three white boys, only just old enough to be driving
stood in the space was moving into.

They looked at me but just stood there,
Narrow minded nearly wide boys,
I edged further in
my metal machine finally forcing them out -

"don't fucking try or I'll send you back home."

My answer was shorter
and just as sweet:
"fuck off"

Later, I wondered whether that had been a free trip
          to Leeds
or Pakistan he had offered me.
If it had been the latter I thought
maybe I'd been hasty in my reply.

Poems by Trudy Blake

UNDER THE MANGO TREE

Under the mango tree
we sit and eat and eat and eat
till our bellies full
Then we filled our baskets
and walked up the road.

THE GRASS

I said to my other half:
how about it-
are you going to get
your ass out there and
cut the grass?

Pardon me?
was his reply.

Let pardon be damned
are you cutting the grass
or what?

Or what, he said.

MY BABY FATHER

He got up, had a shower,
fill up his belly with
me ackee and saltfish, fry
dumplin and cocoa tea.

He was so full that he
stretch and belch. Then he
put on his best suit. As
start walking through
the door, I asked him

You go somewhere man?
Said he was going for a job.
I sit on the chair and watch
the man go out. He look so
handsome that it make my heart
beat fast.

About eleven o'clock I see
Miss Lue Lue, a run come,
so I asked,
-*what wrong Miss Lue Lue,*
somebody dead ?

I come to tell you that
you man a married a strange
women out a Wesley church.

-*Ka-Ka!*

I couldn't believe my earhole.
I nearly drop dead, the man sleep
here last night, whisper his babblings
into my ears, now I hear the
son-of-a-bitch a marry someone else!

I stand at the corner of the streer
thinking, what to do?
The man drive pass me later
with his new wife. she look
so cocky. Hope she break
his ass.

Watching Walter Mosely and Teddy Hayes in the throws of heated debate on the use versus over use of formula in Chester Himes' detective series, (backstage in Lewisham Theatre, celebrating the '*Word*' festival) it suddenly struck me that black detective novelists are akin to black pearls. A rare breed.

Black British detective novelists I'm sure exist. But probably in the depths of some obscure alternative book shop in the outer Hebrides. Underneath the bottom shelf in the dusty box highlighted in green neon marker:
'Clearence -All Vanity Publications !!
Half of the Marked Sale Price! Beat that
for unbeatable value!!!"

Teddy is a native New Yorker transplanted to British soil with roots climbing liberally in both the literary, film and music scene. He has cross-fertilized his *art* by producing a CD sound track inspired by the characters and events that take place in his debut detective novel, '*Blood Red Blues'*.

Like Teddy I always aim to keep one step ahead of the competition, it's a great marketing tool for a black detective novelist and his whole idea is to break into a mainstream audience. I recall Teddy saying,to Mosely, *"Thank God for Elvis, because of him, anything that's got soul can crossover and make huge bucks-Elvis man! He was the ultimate crossover King."*

Teddy's personality grows on you like ivy. He does have a point, there is no reason why he can't be the next Michael Jackson on the literary scene.

Jacqueline Asafu-Adjaye

_____

NEW YORK CITY

Shogun relaxed in the warm flowing water and thought about miracles. He had previously never believed in miracles but if someone asked him now he would have to say that he had gotten it all wrong. After all, wasn't he living proof that miracles happened? Here he was under twenty five and livin extra large already. He was in demand. Like now as he sat in the jacuzzi with these two beautiful women freaking him off.

"You like this, Gun?" Chandra asked as she stroked his penis back and forth while licking his left nipple.

Shogun simply nodded and smiled. Peaches kissed his face intermittently and thrust her long pink tongue into his ear.

"Stand up," Chandra said.

He did as she asked without question.

She reached out with a manicured hand and took a dollop of honey from a jar on a table near the edge of the jacuzzi. She wiped the honey on his organ and then began to suck it off.

Peaches held a glass of champagne up to his lips and, as he drank deeply, bit his nipples, first one and then the other.

Chandra eased him down into the water, straddled him and placed him inside her and began to gyrate vigorously. Of the two women she was the more aggressive. She didn't really like Peaches but what could she do. Shogun liked threesomes and she knew that if she didn't play it his way, he would get someone else who would. So she took what she could get. Peaches on the other hand was more laid back. She never pushed. Just did all the right things at the right times. To Shogun they complimented each other perfectly.

Peaches positioned herself directly behind Shogun and reached around each of his shoulders and started to squeeze his nipples. To be honest he was tired. They had been going at it most of the day. As a result of the two women's expert manipulation of his body parts Shogun had been ejaculating like it was going out of style. He felt sleep coming on just when the phone rang. Peaches handed him the mobile.

"Yeah," he spoke lazily into the phone.

It was Man O War.

"Don't forget about later," War reminded him.

"What time ?" Shogun asked.

"Four thirty," War said.

"What time is it now?" Shogun asked.

"Almost four," War told him.

"Shit. I'll be there, don't worry."

"Don't be late, Gun. This is a big move, yeah, we're going to make a serious move that's going to kick us right to the top of the music production food chain, yeah.

"I feel you," Shogun stated using his latest bit of rapspeak.

"OK," Man O War said and hung up.

Shogun relaxed back into the jacuzzi.

"Gotta go, got an appointment," he said.

"You coming back, right?" Chandra wanted to know.

"Yeah, but it's going to be late. I'll check you later."

He was satisfied sexually. Now he wanted to get into a creative frame of mind.

He and War had business to do. He thought about this as Peaches washed him down. As he stepped out of the jacuzzi Chandra dried him off with a thick green double fluffy bath towel. He thought about what kind of lyrics he would use for their new project. He was a first class rap lyricist. Everyone said his skills were a gift. He wasn't sure how he did it himself. He just did it. A gift from God. Even as a young kid back in London with his uncle who was a calypsonian playing melodies on the guitar, Shogun would step up and make up lyrics. At ten he was as good as some popular calypsonians. Once he even got to meet the greatest calypsonian of them all, The Mighty Sparrow at the Notting Hill Carnival. They even did a tune together. Yeah, words were his gift. He had started writing rap and dancehall lyrics using the name Shakespeare, but decided that Shogun fitted him better. After all, back in the olden days of Japan no one was mightier than the Shogun.

He walked into the other room and started to pick out an outfit for the day from his seemingly endless wardrobe of designer clothes. He always tried to match his gear according to the place he was going. Today he was going to Harlem. The home of the funkiest brothas in the world. They loved him in Harlem, even though he was from London. His acceptance in America's number one famous black ghetto was something he was extremely proud of. A few months ago he was invited to a cipher in Harlem at the world famous Apollo Theatre. In the rap world an invitation to the uptown cipher was like being invited to a command performance in front of the Queen of England. At the cipher, all of the Harlem rappers would get together and freestyle. On the day he was asked, he was on the stage with the elite of the rap world. There was a boxing ring in the middle of the stage and rappers would jump in two at a time and try to knock each other out with lyrics, the crowd being the judges. The rappers started to freestyle, throwing lyrics this way and that, twisting, bending, breaking and turning words and phrases inside out. Shogun found himself in the middle of the ring doing his thing and holding his own. When he finished, even the other rappers gave him a standing ovation. Yeah, Harlem, New York was the place to be.

For his gear that day, he choose a black and gold Fubu top with black corduroy pants, black and tan Nikes and a black Kangol cap. He checked himself in the mirror and knew he looked good. Damn good. As he heard an old man in a Harlem bar say once, he was "ready for Freddy." He felt good, too, as he began to spout lyrics as naturally as rain falling from the sky on a cloudy day.

"You remember what we talked about?" Chandra said, sticking her head inside his bedroom and interrupting his flow.

Damn, he was tired of her now. He wished she would just hurry up, get her shit together and go, but the silly cow kept on talking.

"I need something so I can come to you whenever you want me. Something dependable. Just a Chevy or Ford, nothing fancy." Chandra looked around over her shoulder to make sure Peaches wasn't lurking around the door, listening.

"Like I told you, I'll take care of it, yeah," Shogun said.

She ran her hand against his crotch and kissed him on the neck. But his mind was on other things. She sensed it and backed off. Shogun's mind reverted back to lyrics. As he finished dressing he continued humming one of his latest creations.

"Got to get the goodies while the goodies are hot
Depend on me to hit your G-spot
I'm a poet, a prophet a guru a sage
Expandin your consciousness, takin you to the next stage."

He decided not to take his new Jeep up into Harlem because if he decided to get high he didn't want the police to stop and hassle him. As sure as not they would see him, a young black man driving a new jeep and automatically think he was a drug dealer. So he had Peaches call to get him a limo.

Uptown it was still early, only 4:45pm, but the sun was already showing signs of starting to set in the clear January sky. Even though it was the middle of winter and cold as hell, every now and again rays of sunshine would bite through the frosty urban wilderness to share a little of its warmth with the residents of Harlem like the pope giving absolution to a group of jailhouse sinners.

Part time minister Sister Sally Henley stood on a

Harlem street corner with her sixty seven year old eyes cast up towards the sky. What worried Sister Sally was that it might rain before all of the food she had prepared had been served out. The weather man had forecast a clear day, but the rheumatism in Sister Sally's hands had told her differently and they never lied. Her hands were aching between her finger joints. Rain was definitely on the way. She just hoped it would wait until the food had been served.

Sister Sally was what you might call a professional do-gooder if there is such a thing. For the past five years, on the second Sunday of each month after service, she would drive the church van filled with five or six different dishes she had prepared to some street corner location God had guided her to, where she would set up the church van to feed the hungry. It wasn't an elaborate set-up by any means. Just a few tables, some steaming pots of food, paper plates, plastic cups, forks and spoons. But over the many years she had been doing this the people of Harlem had come to know her. Most people called her Sister Soul Food, which was the phrase coined by the Amsterdam News, the African American newspaper which had featured her several times. These articles helped raise Sister Sally donations from big corporations, which had enabled her to have several hundred turkeys slaughtered for Thanksgiving and put on a feast for the needy of Harlem.

With Sister Sally it was always the same routine. Her slogan was "Take a plate and thank the Lord." Her mission was a pure one. She just wanted to give a few hungry souls a little nourishment as an enticement to see the guiding light that would take them straight to Jesus.

She squinted up into the clear sky again and then back to the food she had prepared. Sister Sally was an excellent cook. In fact she had worked as a cook in a private school for over twenty years to support and raise her three children. She took the job after her husband Henry was killed in a knife fight over a green-eyed creole woman named Esther Jackson from Baton Rouge, Louisiana, back in the late sixties.

Sister Sally surveyed her handiwork on the tables before her. There were five pots altogether. One pot was filled with stew beef and vegetables, one with smoked neck bones, one with cabbage, one with rice and another huge pot was full of black eyed peas.

There was a patter of excitement among the hungry as a long black limousine drove up in front of the building where Sister Sally had set up her tables. When a young man jumped out of the car somebody yelled:

"Yo, it's Shogun y'all."

Sister Sally was too busy dishing out food to pay much notice. Besides, in her sixty seven years on this earth she had seen enough limousines to last her a lifetime. She also knew that some of the fanciest cars were owned by some of the worst people God ever gave breath to, so she wasn't the least bit impressed or interested in who the handsome young man was or wasn't. Besides, she knew that limousine or no limousine, it wouldn't matter much on the Day of Judgment. On that great day when whoever the young man was stood before the good Lord in heaven, he would be as naked as the day he was born. All the limousines, big houses, important jobs and everything else most people accumulated in this world and held near and dear wouldn't amount to a hill of pinto beans.

She only looked up and took any notice at all

because of the noise. She saw the young man wave and then quickly run into the building, before turning her mind back to food, rheumatism and rain.

Shogun took the elevator to the fifth floor. He glanced at his gold Rolex. He was twenty minutes late. He readied his mind for a dirty look from Man O War.

He loved War like a brother. They had been mates since they were barely old enough to walk and were as close as blood and bone.

The door buzzer was answered by a smiley-faced man who he knew.

"Hey wha'ppen," Shogun greeted as he crossed the threshold into the nicely decorated and furnished apartment. "Where's War?"

"Not here yet," the man said.

"That's good," Shogun said and relaxed.

"Want to see it?" the man gleamed at the briefcase in his hand.

"You got it?"

"Right here."

"Ain't we going to wait for War?"

"Of course. I bet you've never seen that much cash before, huh?"

"Yeah, OK," Shogun said expectantly.

The smiley-faced man led Shogun into the next room where he opened the briefcase in the light of an open window. Inside was filled to the brim with green bills in neat bundles.

The smiley-faced man grinned. "It's exciting just to see it and it's nice just to touch it, go ahead," he coaxed.

Shogun smiled. He picked up one of the bundles.

The smiley-faced man was right. It did feel nice to touch all that cash. Nicer than Shogun had expected. It sent a tingly feeling through his body. Shogun leaned forward to pick up another bundle when suddenly everything went black.

The blow from the axe severed Shogun's head cleanly from his body. The severed head fell off his shoulders and rolled out of the open window.

Sister Sally was still looking up into the sky for rain when she saw something fall out of the window above. She wasn't sure what it was, but she knew Harlem well enough to know people were liable to throw anything out of a window - shoes, garbage, TVs... But when it dropped right into the middle of her pot of black eyed peas, Sister Sally couldn't believe her own eyes.

A human head with eyes bucked out and looking straight at her, as big as life itself.

Sister Sally couldn't even find voice enough to scream, she just fainted on the spot.

'Brixton Rock' is Alex Wheatle's first novel and won the 1999 New London Writers Prize. Wheatle was born in South London in 1963. After leaving school at the age of 16, he became an apprentice carpenter. A serious bout of pneumonia in 1982 prompted him to leave the building sites and take up indoor work in the engineering trade. He started writing by sending encouraging letters to friends who found themselves in prison in the early 1980's.

The Times journalist **Nicky Milson** has a few words to say on Wheatle's 'Brixton Rock' ...

'It's a triumph bearing a striking resemblence to Graham Greene's Brighton Rock. The main difference is that Brixton Rock is very funny. Brixton Rock is a pacey document of teenage angst which is why the pockets of humour prove to be such a triumph. This is a debut novel which confirms its author a pro in prose.'

RING THE ALARM
Saturday 22 March 1980

Brenton Brown's last day of being a juvenile coincided with the sound-system event of the year, the Gold Cup competition - a tournament in which the top kick-arse sounds in London would musically cross swords in Brixton Town Hall.

Brenton and Floyd had to be there to support their favourite sound system - Moa Anbessa. Everyone had been debating about the contest for weeks, and fast-talking hustlers, who in the last few weeks became friendly with the promoters of this dance, laid out odds on who would win.

The two spars departed home at six-thirty in the evening, hoping to arrive at the venue early to beat the expected ramjam at the entrance. Apparently, many other roots rockers had the same idea, because the 35 bus, routed to Acre Lane, Brixton, brimmed to over-capacity.

The two friends claimed their seats on the upper deck, taking a sense of identity in the red, gold and green belts and scarves that everybody seemed to be wearing. "Look like this dance is gonna ram", commented Brenton.

Floyd, confident in a grey trench coat, black Stetson and black polo-neck sweater, attempted to make eye-contact with the girls around him. "It's true, Gold Cup dance is always ram. I just hope Bassa can win it. I've heard the sound men have been studio and cut nuff dub-plates."

One beret-topped guy apparently could't wait for the music to start. For in the rear of the upper deck, taking up most of the room on the double seat, he had his fingers on the control of an enormous Brixton suitcase - which was more like a London trunk. He was playing a tape of all the latest reggae releases from

Jamaica, massaging the appetite of the roots heads.

A fearful conductor emerged from the stairwell, wearing a cap and his ticket machine strapped to his chest. He stole a glance at the DJ's luggage, then eyed the vociferous passengers before slipping back down the stairs.

The conductor was a picture of relief as the throng of black youngsters vacated the bus at Brixton Town Hall. A mass of people grouped near the entrance of the Hall, blocking the path of pedestrians, watching a big white rental van park awkwardly near a zebra crossing.

Walking alongside Brenton, Floyd clocked the disorganised scene and nudged him. "That's Coxone man just reach. Yeah, I recognise Festus the operator."

Brenton turned his head sharply to look at the proud-visaged Festus, who resembled a general arriving at the scene of battle, confident of victory.

All of a sudden, the shutters at the back of the van were raised to reveal about ten black youngsters, none of whom looked old enough to drain liquor. They bullfrogged out of the van and vigorously started their evening's work. They were the 'boxboys' of the sound system, responsible for the lifting and carrying of all the heavy equipment.

A gravel-like voice of Jamaican accent boomed out, "Mind yuh back, mind yuh back." As the double doors at the entrance swung open, the boxboys bumped the huge boxes, the size of double wardrobes, into the arena.

Meanwhile, Brenton and Floyd queued up to gain entry, hoping to sight Biscuit, Finnley, Coffin Head or anybody else from their posse. There was another liquor-belly man, dressed in army garb and sporting a hairstyle akin to Jimi Hendrix's, receiving the entry tax while shouting in a Kingstonian twang: "One pound fifty fe come in. One pound fifty fe come in. If yuh nuh 'ave it, fuck off an' remove from the gate. One pound fifty fe come in."

The two brethrens paid their tax and made their way to the arena, with Brenton looking here and there, wary of the presence of Terry Flynn, and Floyd, wha'appening and greeting fellow Brixtonians he knew. Three threats from the doorman later, Brenton and Floyd finally met up with Biscuit, who was crocodiling a Mars bar, Finnley and Coffin Head - the owner of the squarest forehead this side of black London.

This was the sound owners' busiest time. Cables of electric wire resembled a giant man's helping of multi-coloured spaghetti. Each of the four competing sounds claimed a corner, scowling at each other as they connected record decks, pre-amplifiers, echo chambers and the like, while the boxboys were busy stringing up the speaker boxes. The only space near the walls where you couldn't find a speaker box was either at the entrance, or where the sound ëcontrol towersí were placed. This was usually aluminium casing, about head height, housing all the amplifiers and the extras topped off by a record deck.

Floyd and his posse were spellbound, like many others, watching Moa Anbessa controls get pieced together. While the youngsters stared at their heroes, the hall filled up rapidly as the sound guys applied the finishing touches to their routine.

The crowd savoured the almost ritualistic atmosphere, feeling a sense of belonging as they marvelled at the red, gold and green colours. Rastafarians wore their long locks proudly and black females adorned in their African-type dresses, added a spice of culture to the event. Pictures of the late Emperor, Haile Selassie of Ethiopia, hung or were sellotaped to the walls. The aroma of West Indian cuisine drifted through the air, blending with the exotic breath of marijuana. There was a serious trade at the bar, where strong beers and soft drinks were selling at inflated prices.

The dreadlocked operator of the Moa Anbessa sound drew the crowd's attention. He carefully placed a record on the rotating table and spoke into the microphone.

"Test one, test one. One, two, microphone test."

The amplified voice was a cue for the people massing around the lobby to rapidly converge in the hall, where they watched the operator finger-wipe the needle of the record deck, producing a heavy scratching sound that earthquaked from the speakers. Looking very proud and clocking the crowd around him, the Moa Anbessa operator announced through the microphone, "In tune to the A1 champion sound of de world - Moa Anbessa!"

Then he proceeded to play a record, which delighted his followers. Within half an hour, every sound was ready, so the competition commenced. Soferno B, Jah Shaka, Sir Coxone and Moa Anbessa were about to compete for the prestigious title of 'Champion Sound of London'.

The lights in the hall were switched off, which acted as a stimulant for excited youngsters to start shouting, jumping and skanking whenever their favourite sound played a record. Everyone became infected with the skanking vibe, hotstepping on the stage, in the lobby and even in the queue leading up to the bar.

The hall juddered to the relentless drum and bass rhythms of Johnny Osbourne, The Twinkle Brothers, Gregory Isaacs, Dennis Brown and other top-ranking artistes from Jamaica. A lone rastaman grabbed some roots-heads' attention by holding a bongo drum between his knees and trying to keep in time to the music. Skankers in black tracksuits with red and green rims showed off their new moves and party pieces, with onlookers marvelling at the way they controlled their bodies. Most of the youngsters besieged the control towers, captivated by their heroes and cheering every time they were commanded to.

At around eleven o'clock, the competition came to a climax, and the judges declared Jah Shaka the winner. Jah Shaka's followers hollered and whooped their approval, along with the illegal bookmakers. Floyd and his posse, backed up by others, barked their disappointment as they threaded their way out of the building.

The scene at the bus stops could have been the warm streets of downtown Kingston as Brenton and Floyd bade laters to their spars. Brenton looked forward to the Clint Eastwood film on telly that night, but Floyd felt the night wasn't over yet. "Char man, Bassa got robbed. Dem judge are crooks, man. Bassa played the most wicked music. I reckon some of them are in the Shaka posse anyway." Brenton agreed, scanning the crowd for any sight of his nemesis, Terry Flynn.

The two spars observed the hordes of reggae-heads jostling and pushing to get aboard a 37 bus. Floyd had an agitated appearance on his dial. "I don't feel like going home, man." This was the last thing

Brenton wanted to hear. He had arranged to go out early next morning with his sister to a Sunday market in East London. Juliet had promised her brother she would buy something for him to wear for his birthday present. Unaware of this, Floyd mentioned, "I have hardly got no herb left, so I might go and check out Chemist." He lives off Brixton Hill, and then we'll go and see what Sharon is saying. She might have a rave."

Although reluctant to go, Brenton tried hard not to show his aversion, knowing Floyd always wanted company when he was stepping the streets of Brixton. So the spars turned right off Acre Lane and trod up Brixton Hill, passing St Matthew's Church. With his spirits rising up again, Floyd remarked, "Did you see Druffy? He's dread. He should do something about his hair, man. When he was skanking, all dust and rust was coming from his head top. His hair's as dry as the African desert. I told him 'cos the shops are closed, he should go petrol station an buy some oil and slap it on his head quick time."

Brenton laughed out loud. "Yeah, it's true, but he don't care, does he? He should at least wear a bloody hat or something."

"What about Biscuit in his 1950's trousers? Doesn't he know that man nowadays wear trousers that reach down to his shoes? I don't know where he's going with dem three-quarter trousers. Check him to me 'bout he's gonna check some gal later on.' He ain't checking nutten with those trousers."

Brenton laughed again then stopped abruptly. He'd seen something to alarm him - a beast van travelling slowly towards them, just passing Brixton College.

"Floyd, look, radication squad."

Floyd glanced up. "Shit, stay cool and step it over on the other side of the road. If we have to chip, then we can burn across the grass and into the flats."

The duo crossed the road, both sensing the dark cloud of danger in the shape of a white van overswilling with pigs. Brenton and Floyd kept the vehicle in their sights as they ambled innocently up the hill. The van performed a U-turn and neared the teenagers. "Stay cool",

Floyd advised. "Remember, pigs can't burn as fast as us."

The white van pulled up alongside them and out stepped a double-chinned pig. This action prompted the driver of the van to accelerate until he was abreast of the black youths. The pig trotted up to the teenagers and oinked spitefully, "So where are you two niggers going tonight? Planning a burglary? Or are you waiting for a little old dear to walk by so you can nick her purse?"

"Who are you calling nigger, you big white shit."

Floyd's sharp eyes spotted some movement in the van. As the officer closed in, Brenton and Floyd backed off onto the grass verge. "You're a cheeky wog, aren't you? You won't be so cheeky inside a cell."

"Run!"

The two brethren burned as hard as they could as the van emptied out another four hungry pigs. Floyd led the way, heading for the flats. Cars stopped on Brixton Hill as motorists watched the beast being outpaced by the two youngsters. Gaining a lead into the council estate, Floyd and Brenton leaped, without thought or hesitation, into a large grey metal rubbish bin.

Fearfully they waited submerged in garbage and trying to murder their heavy breathing. The sounds of heavy trotters made Brenton and Floyd keep very still. When the beast arrived in the forecourt they hovered around for a while, with two of them searching the balconies. Brenton and Floyd could hear one of the officers grunt after a period of ten minutes-"The charcoal bandits have fucking disappeared. Come on, let's go. There's many more coons out there in the sea."

The radication squad dispersed from the estate, leaving a nervous Brenton and Floyd up to their necks in black bags full of rubbish. Floyd whispered to his spar, "You think the beast have gone?"

"I don't hear them, but even if they are still around, I can't stay in this shit for too long. I stink. Which one of these blocks does Chemist live in?"

"The one just in front of us."

"So why the fuck didn't we go there straight away?" hissed Brenton, glaring at his spar.

"Too risky. Say the beast caught us at Chemist's yard, he would have got pull as well cos he's got a big bag of herb at his yard with all scales and ting," explained Floyd, sniffing and catching scent of something that might have died in prehistoric times.

Brenton took a peep over the top of the large bin. "Hey Floyd, come on, man. I can smell shit but I can't smell no pigs."

They climbed out of the bin and stealthily made their way to the block of flats nearby, checking behind them all the time. They eventually reached Chemist's front door and Floyd gently slapped the letter box. Seconds later, the front door opened to reveal a spliff-smoking Chemist, adorned in many gold chains and heavy gold rings. "Quick, close the door."

'Changing Britannia', presents a ground breaking history of the black British experience over the past half century and more. Edited by Roxy Harris and Sarah White much of its commentary provides the reader with a thought provoking and indispensable chronical of modern British history.

Seven prominent black Britons from a diverse range of backgrounds talk through their struggles for political social and cultural freedom. Amongst its contributors are: Linton Kwesi Johnson, Alex Pascall, Colin Prescod, Garth Crooks, Pearl Conner-Mogotsi and Courtenay Griffiths.

Linton Kwesi Johnson is an internationally acclaimed dub poet. Jamaican born, he arrived in England at the tender age of eleven. The author of four books of poetry, he his released nine recordings of his work, many of them in collaboration with Dennis Bovell and his dub band. Linton formed his own record label in 1981, LKJ Records and has since received a number of literary awards.

Linton Kwesi Johnson on his early experience in Britain and his first moves into poetry, public performance-and music.

It was in the Panthers, when I discovered literature, black literature, because we were encouraged to read. In fact there were books that we studied, chapter and verse, going through them systematically. One of them was Capitalism and Slavery by Dr Eric Williams, the other was Frantz Fanon's The Wretched of the Earth. And the third one was The Black Reconstruction by W.E.B. Du Bois. We had a little library and we were allowed to borrow books, and one of books that I borrowed was a book called The Souls of Black Folk by W.E.B. Du Bois. That was a book. It was one of the most beautiful things I ever read. It just, blew my mind. It was about the experiences of blacks in America after slavery had been abolished and the language- I was struck by the language. The poetic language of Du Bois' writing. I remember one phrase from that book. He talked about 'The Colour Line' the problem of the twentieth century was the problem of the colour line. And after I read that book I just wanted to read more. To be able to write and to express my own ideas and my own feelings and my experiences about growing up in England.

―――――――――――――――

Garth Crooks on being prominent in football and sport.

It wasn't until I hit 13 or 14 that school represented an environment for real hard core education which meant I had to work as hard with the books as I did with the ball. At first that horrified me because I got pleasure out of playing with a football and being able to pit my wits against other players who were often older and stronger than me. But I wasn't too happy about the books, the academic situation, because I wasn't that gifted and I wasn't that sharp and I was going to have to work very very hard. All the teachers thought that I had it and I became very unpopular with teachers because I was lazy and I wasn't prepared to apply myself. I

It was only until a wonderful headmaster named Mr Edward Moss, a wonderful old man, brought me in one day to his office. He was tired of giving me the cane and sat me down saying, "You've got to understand, if you're going to have a chance of being what you want to be, you're going to have to learn to conform".

And I remember those days, I those words to this day but at the time I didn't fully understand what he meant. However I remember the expression on his face. It was an expression of desperation mixed in with fear and evaporating hope, I'd never seen him like that before. I went away remembering what he had said 'if you want to achieve, if you want to be what you really want to be, you're going to have to apply yourself'. I recall asking my teacher, "What did he mean, apply yourself?" It came back to that old adage: work. 'You're going to have to work,'. I couldn't get out of it. I couldn't get away from this thing of work.

It was strange because that dogged me right throughout my football career. When I joined Stoke City at sixteen, Gordon Banks, who sadly had a car accident had lost the use of one of his eyes. It was his left eye. He suffered this terrible trauma in his life in that one day, everything that he had and worked for was gone. Gordon took over the youth team at Stoke City. I was one of those youth members working with a great someone that I'd seen play. I loved the man. I identified with Banks because he was a brilliant football player Just as Mr

Edward Moss had said, he remarked "Garth, you've got a lot of talent, but you're going to have to work".

Watching Gordon work, day in-day-out, whether it was sunny, raining or snowing, it didn't matter, he was always putting in. Always putting in, putting in time, putting in effort and I think it was he more than anyone that finally convinced me, that if I was going to have any career in the modern professional game, it was going to be playing the English way, not the French way or the Brazilian way or the Italian way, the English way.

I was born in England. I was schooled in England, if I wanted to have a career in professional football in England, I was going to have to play their way. I had no intention of going to play in Paris. I had no one-way ticket to Paris or anywhere else for that matter.

Alex Pascall was born in Grenada, he immigrated to England in 1959. A teacher, performer and promoter of Caribbean music and history. He produced and presented Britain's first black community BBC radio programme, called 'Black Londoners' in 1974. He chaired the Notting Hill Carnival Arts Committee for five years and is currently working on the development of the Caribbean Heritage Project in Greenwich. He writes on the historic radio programme 'Black Londoners'.

Music policy, I agreed not to play American music.

Americans were getting enough coverage black or otherwise. I said let me play preferably calypso and deep African-rooted music. Here and there I played a reggae track because Steve Barnard was already there putting out the reggae so why should I go into conflict? I remember that record 'Sugar Boom Boom' pretty well because it was the first record that broke the deadlock between the people of the south and the people of the north. It was the first time Reggae Time played calypso. Steve Barnard before wouldn't play it. He couldn't play it because they would have roasted him. We had this island north-south divide that was frightening.

How could you give me a programme for one and a half hours to meet what is called Britain's black community? Look at the volume of people that you're giving me to deal with. I had to make sure that I put a little snip of everything. The French Creole went on. People used to sit their children and family down in an evening, 'You have to listen to Black Londoners!' I meet people and young children that grew up with Black Londoners, 'I grew up with you, you know boy'. I'd say, 'That's nice to know'. He continued, 'My father used to make damn sure that I didn't move away from the radio.' That was good. It was all we had.

Six-year-old Michael La Rose and his family left the sunny climes of Trinidad for England in 1963. By 1975 Michael formed the People War Sound System with the help of his brother and friends. It was destined to be amongst the first sound systems to play from a moving truck at Nottingham Hill Carnival in 1978.

He works with New Beacon Books and is currently an Inspector with the Health and Safety Executive.

Michael La Rose speaks on the rise of the sound system in popular culture and social life.

What was sound system culture? First of all, you made your own boxes, (speaker enclosures)and amplifiers. The best sound systems were those who had people in them who were carpenters and electrical engineers. They had the best sound systems. The actual sound was very important. The tops, I'll just say how it is and how I know it was and you can ask me later on what it means. The tops (treble) had to be clear. The voice (mid range) part of it, had to be very clear, the chip had to be very sharp, just as the bass line had to lick your chest-knock you over. We used to use one deck and a toaster to fill the gaps. The toaster is what we call now an MC, our heroes at that time were toasters called I Roy, U Roy and Big Youth.

The currency then was records. There were record shops that sold imported tracks from Jamaica. We called them pre-releases meaning records available before they were released in Britain. But we shortened that word to 'pre' or 'pres'- because those records were very precious and you not want another person to have it, due to the competition. You tore the labels off so that nobody else could get it. If someone looked at your deck and looked at the record, they would not know what the record was. I''ve got a lot of records at home where I don't know who the artist is.

How could we afford these records? They were very expensive, especially the imported records. How could we afford the material for the boxes? How could we afford the equipment? This was expensive heavy duty equipment. How was it possible? I have been thinking about this very recently.

Remember we were youths, most of us were either at school, or unemployed-very few had work. But those who did work, got HP, and we also put our money together collectively. We also stole the equipment.

There is a film called Babylon, about a sound system. It is the only film I know about a sound system in Britain. It's directed by Franco Rosso. There is a particular scene, where we all laughed because, that is what really happened to us. The characters were stealing a speaker from a train station, you know the PA system and that's what happened to us. We did that We took the whole thing, unscrewed a bracket off the wall, and ran away with the speaker. By any means necessary was the attitude to getting sound equipment and that's what happened. If you ever get a chance, see that film- Babylon. That scene was realistic.

Sorrelle
MILLIE MURRAY

Pretty simple enough story: boy meets girl and they fall in love. There is only one snag though, the girl in question, Sorrelle is black and the boy Arun is Asian. And for some reason this relationship is set to cause friction between parents, friends and even strangers on the street.

Through the eyes of our black teenage heroine Sorrelle, we see how a pretty simple relationship becomes a complex minefield when racial intolerance takes over the ideal of multi-cultural harmony and sadly wins.

The light and witty approach of the author belies the serious issues and also manages to get to the roots of teenage love and angst without getting too mushy.

'New Nation' (book review section)

THE RESTAURANT

The Cantonese restaurant was half full. There was a table to the right of us made up to seat at least twelve people. We sat at a small table for four, but it was just us two. Arun ordered for us, but I looked at the menu before the waiter took it and the prices were worryingly high.

"What would you like to drink?" Arun asked me.

"Fresh orange juice."

"That's it?"

I nodded. The waiter took our order and the menus and left.

Sitting back in my chair, I thought about the different reactions from people when I told them I was going to dinner with Arun. When I told my mum and dad it just so happened that mum was moaning at my dad about him not taking her out for a meal as a treat.

"Mum, talking about going out for dinner, Arum's taking me out on Saturday as a way of saying thank you for helping out at his barbecue."

"Really? That's nice of him."

"Who is he?' enquired Dad.

"A friend of Trenton's who lives in Chigwell."

That explanation wasn't enough for Dad. "Who else is going?"

"Just me and him dad."

"Bertie, drop it now,'"said Mum.

"But Donna, Rell is my only girl child and I want to know about any man taking her anywhere. Look how many girls are being abducted and abused and killed by just innocently going out to dinner with their brother's friends."

Mum and I both burst out laughing, "Oh Dad, stop it! Look, you can get his mobile phone number off Trenton, so you'll be able to contact me at any time."

Dad growled something I couldn't make out. When I told Trenton, he thought Arun was wasting his money on me.

"You're so feisty, Trenton. He's done more for me than you've ever done for as long as I've known you."

"But it's the truth. When I think of all those beautiful girls he knows, and he's taking you out! The guy's gone..."He pointed to his forehead.
'Just shut up, you! ' I was annoyed with him.

I told Priya the next day when she came round.
"He's-taking-you-out-for-a-meal!" She almost shouted at me, pointed her finger in an accusing way in my face.
"Look, Priya. All the guy's doing is taking me out for some food, end of story." I threw my arms out wide.
"But what about me? You know how much I fancy him!" She wailed.
"What about you? It was me that was slogging my guts out sorting out the food-you swanning about like royalty," I retorted.

She stopped for a moment and I could tell she was cooking up something.

"Rell, this is what you do. Call him and tell him that I'll be coming with you on Saturday. That's it, he's obviously forgotten that I was helping you. It's a simple mistake, anyone could make it."

Puzzled, I said to her, "What are you talking about? You've lost me."
Priya then plunged into some convoluted story about why Arun had invited me, and why she should be going as well.

"No," I said firmly and finally. Priya and I never really fell out, but there was times when I had to put her in her place, like now for instance.
She sussed I wasn't taking any rubbish from her so she changed her tune.
"He doesn't fancy you or anything, so don't get any ideas."

"I could've told you that. It's no big deal, this dinner date, so calm yourself down."

"Phew!"

"...next weekend," said Arun.

"Pardon?" I had been lost in my thoughts and had not been paying attention to what he was saying.

"I said my parents are back next weekend."

"Oh lovely."

His shiny black hair kept flopping over his forehead. Now he pushed it back and looked at me seriously. It wasn't the vulnerable look I'd noticed at the party, more a sort of searching look. My stomach did a somersault. "Calm down, Rell!" I told myself, and began chatting up about some film I'd seen the weekend before. Gradually I relaxed. He was easy to talk to.

Walking around Leicester Square afterwards, I thanked Arun fo the meal. I'd had a great evening. The only thing that marred it was the group of young Asian people sitting near us in the restaurant. They kept looking over and they were obviously talking about us. think Arun knew what they were saying, but being a bit of a gentleman, he didn't tell me a thing. But their body language was giving it all away. I was sure what the main topic on their agenda was- why was a nice Asian boy out with a black girl? One girl in particular was giving me the eyeball, so I eyeballed her back- in fact, I wanted to ask her what her problem was, but I didn't want to drag, Arum into any confrontation.

We sat in the car outside my door for a few minutes. Arun turned to face me. "You know, Rell, there's something...different about you."

"Oh yeah? Different from what?"

"I don't know. From other girls. You seem sot of laid-back. As if you know your own mind."

I thought of those overdressed, gushing girls who'd been all over him at his party. Maybe he had a point!

"Well, I hope I do," I told him.

He gave me one of his searching looks. "Could I see you again, Rell?"

I didn't stop to think. I said, "Yes."

Bittersweet
KAREN McCARTHY

Karen McCarthy has worked in book publishing and the media as an editor, broadcaster and publicist. She has worked as a freelance journalist and researcher for BBC Radio 4, the World Service and Carlton Television in the documentaries department. She edited 'Bittersweet' an anthology of black women's contemporary poetry for the Women's Press.

'Passport' by Karen McCarthy is an excerpt taken from, 'Bittersweet'.

McCarthy in an interview with the 'Weekly Journal' describes the impact of 'Bittersweet', "It is dedicated to phenomenal women. Ordinary women whose wounds have healed into poems and whose words catch and burst in your throat, taking your breath away."

PASSPORT

You are not indelible.
I saw the photograph: your pre-independence passport-(1957)-when you passed port.
Your face-out of place. Looking freer then.
Tick-tock. Bee-bop. Discord. A-chord. Recall

The un-rub out-able record.

5-5,6-6,7,8,9. Quick time.
Numbers numb me. Hide the memory.
I see you before you saw me (Tick-tock, take-stock).

I saw you before you see me (Take stock, tick-tock).
Can I recognize the slick zoot suit?
Looking fine, see your skin shine.
Yeah, looks like you knew how to have a good time.

And then. Forty years.
Forty years. And then.
Multiple patriarch. Mr Mack.Daddy.
You are no Johnny come lately.
Johnny gone long time.
I never saw him before.
But you know who he is.

With the use of an old borrowed word processor, 19-year-old Suheir Hammad began to type out her thoughts. Frustrated by so many things-family life to the political climate-Hamad began to tell her story in order to understand her own identity.

In this soul-searching narrative, Hammad touches on alcoholism, sexist attitudes, race, and culture. As a young Arab raised in Brooklyn she is a product of two cultures. In this memoir Hammad, as part of the hip hop generation, gives respect to that art form and to the tradition from which it grew.

Suheir Hammad has put her soul into words, revealing the growing pains of a young woman

---

RAIN

There's this story that comes down to me all the time, wet. It don't come down like some big old rain storm, with thunder and lightning, that drives cars off the road in the middle of autumn nights. It ain't one of them pleasant summer showers either, them that can clean city streets in the middle of a hot working day. The kind of wet I'm talking about is the annoying frustrating wet that barely manages to layer the concrete, yet somehow frizzes my hair into on big bush. The kind of teasing wet that seems to serve no other purpose than to let you know its there. You know the type-It makes you look stupid to hold an umbrella and has people arguing over whether or not it's really raining.

This story teases my head just like that, 'cause I know I can't stick out my tongue to taste a rainbow or put out a bucket to catch flying sun beams. Loves to let me know it's there, taunting me, 'cause I am the only one who can see it. Hear it. Smell it. This story laughs at me when I pull out an umbrella to shield my hair and then pinches my face just to let me know it's still around. What's worse about this kind of wet is that every drop hitting the back of my neck has it's own tale to tell.

Colorful drops slip into my ear and travel down to my heart, where they wreak havoc on my system. I tell you that I've never been addicted to any type of drug. Ever. I never had to be. I'm addicted to music. I get high off a beat. Any kind of beat. Them drops hum Sam Cooke to me, while a Public Enemy riff beats the background of my brain. They order me to write about Abdel-Halem Hafez, and how I finally learned my parents' language when I was seventeen, just so I could understand his songs. I fell in love with his songs, and translations ain't no good. English is deficient in the language of love, translations ain't no good.

Them drops sing me into writing about Bob Marley's love of life and my love of his poetic music. They come down to the rhythm of good merengue beat and slide down my body to the pulsing of heated tabla drums. I need to write of how the tabla moves my hips to dance without knowing it. How the tabla sounds like the voice of God on a good day. Them drops from my sweat after I've danced the pain away. They slide off my moving body until I'm left with a floor that needs to be mopped up with the pages of a book.

There's this one drop that burst to life on top my right eyebrow one day. This one wants me to write about my father. The wetness traveled down my face as though I had cried it out of my eyes, as though it hadn't fallen from the sky. sThis is when I tell you about my father's heart of gold and mouth of bile. How my orphaned father - landless, motherless, nationless- can't deal with New York and can't deal with me. The only thing he can deal with is his bottle, and that relationship he cherishes. As though it were Hennesey, and not me, that had come from his loins. My father loves me, I know that now. I also know that he is killing me with his loneliness, his power, his liquor his hate, his love. My orphaned father can't deal with my attitude, my strength, my loneliness, my poetry, my love. He can't deal wit me 'cause I'm just like him. He gave me all of the things that he can't deal with within himself. I'm just like him, only I don't drink. I write, and I cry. I work on only writing.

DROPS. They keep falling on, and I don't have an umbrella to shield me from the wetness. Most have a smell to them, and, through hypnotic gases, I tell you I was raised around the delicious stinks of the Ghetto. Fried plantains and smoked reefers, my mother's stuffed eggplant and the neighbor's pork ribs. Our apartment buildings was always swaying with the smells of the East, the Caribbean, and the South. Them drops soak me till I let you know that the memories of my childhood stink deliciously of fried foods, spoiled fruits, and garbage that was picked up once a week, if the gods of sanitation were in the mood.

The smell of fish...and that time I saw a fish in the sink. I was about ten. My father was cleaning it up to fry, and he simply has it lying there. I thought the fish came in them ready-made filets. Screamed when I saw the creature. Huge, with its head still on, it's cold fish eyes staring up at me. I screamed a loud ass scream, and before I could get another breath of life's air into my lungs, my father's hand slapped down my mouth. I know never to scream from fear in his presence again. My father hates the sound of fear, of female screaming.

Them drops feel pretty good, but I soon feel others. These crawl down into my bra. Demand I sing the song about unwanted attention from men who really appreciate the body of a skinny five-year-old girl. Hard to tell, 'cause I know I can't make none of it up. I know I gotta tell it like I know it. There ain't no fiction here. Truth demands to be told. 'Cause its been shoved down too many throats. I feel like it, taste it, even after the wetness has dried between my breasts. This one needs to be told poetically and carefully, so you don't blame me, and I don't blame myself. I brush this drop away for now. No fiction here. I can't yet write it poetically.

RESTLESS wetness that annoys you into submitting to the will of the word. You know the type. Feels like a broken sprinkler trying to drown the sad grass of a sad park filled with drug tools and other tools of sadness. Don't let you know its coming, soaks you out of nowhere, and you're perfectly dry. The type of musky dampness that you hate 'cause you know you're not in the right place or with the right person to ease it into memory.

It comes in little beads that sometime cut through the skin, to enter your blood stream and lungs as you breathe in life's air. One of them got me on the back of my left knee on day as I was jumping rope. This one, too, had it's own story to tell. The story of frustrated teenage boys. Teenage boys with bad skin and worse attitudes. Teenage boys who had to make me feel like I really was too ugly, too skinny to get any better. That story has the ending already written out, 'cause when I see them boys now it's all, 'Whassup baby? You don't remember me? We used to be so close.' The only close I remember was their nasty breath telling me I was lucky to be with them, and I couldn't tell their girlfriends. That's what I remember.

THE WETNESS sometimes storms my head in the guise of meteor showers, and the heat of it burns my soul until I realise that this story should be told. When my skin is suffering from the heat, words spurt from my spirit in drops of sweat, and I write of longing for a land I have yet to feel under my feet. This tale is part of them all, and it never whispers it's urgency, it shouts it in song. The call to and from Palestine and her love, this is the command that automatically straightens my back and refuses anymore of my tears. But this story need to be told right. It'll be told by my anger and my love. I have to tell it in such a way that I can let you, make you, force you to feel the loss of a land you have never felt under your feet. I sometimes wonder if I'm up to the task of telling it the way it needs to be told. I wonder if I'll live long enough to write the million or so pages needed to explain this love of land. Other times I know I can and will make you, force you to understand what I'm taking about. All in one word. That word has yet to make you wet these pages and soak this soul, so I'll keep writing until I no longer need to.

Just as some drops of wetness are hot and burn, there are those that are cold and freeze. They are the ones that speak the story of Brooklyn, the land that I've lovingly caressed under my feet. My sneakered feet. That story will be told by my walk. My sneakered feet will tell of all the stray dogs I had to kick out of my way home from the bodega on the corner. The crack vials I had to jump over, and the empty forty ounces that rolled under my steps. The streets of Brooklyn and how my Fila sneakers were worn out every couple of months from the concrete, that story. How I used to search that same concrete to find a lone rusty dime with which to buy some Lemonheads or Cherry Bombs. Them are the stories my wet feet will tell...

'Silent Terror' is the disturbing true account of a black American's journey into the horrors of modern-day slavery in Africa. The author's odyssey takes him from New York to the Islamic republic of Mauritania where he comes face-to-face with the Arab's centuries-old practice of enslaving black Africans. Samuel Cotton's research exposes this heinous practice while documenting and analysing the hatred that the Arab minority holds for blacks, both slave and free, in a country where everyone is Muslim.

THE ARRIVAL

It is December twenty-third, and Flight 562 sets down in Dakar, the capital of Senegal. Senegal, the western-most country in Africa, is bordered on the south by Guinea-Bissau and Guinea, on the east by Mali, and on the north across the Senegal River by Mauritania. The independent enclave of Gambia nearly divides the country. What is known as Senegal and Mauritania was at one time one colonial territory before France divided it in two in December 1933. Senegal then became fully independent from France in 1960, the same year that Mauritania achieved its independence.

As I step through the door of the aircraft, the sun is shining brilliantly. A wave of heat washes over me as I put my foot on African soil for the very first time. 'I am home, fathers and mothers! I am HERE! I have come as I said I would!' I feel like shouting. Instead, I say these words silently to my ancestors, my chest almost bursting my heart flooding with emotion.

The ancient one I am calling out to, I wonder who were they? What were their names? What had they looked like? Making my way towards the terminal, I am completely absorbed by thoughts of that African man and woman who, after surviving the hellish voyage across the ocean made love in the loveless world and brought forth the line that would bear the slave name Cotton.

According to my sources, black people remained enslaved in north-western Africa, and that was what I was in Senegal and soon Mauritania to investigate. For the moment, however, I was spending my days and nights living among these strong and resilient refugees in their temporary shelters and camps. And something was happening to me. Living and talking with my Mauritanian brothers and sisters in Senegal was having a profound effect on my consciousness.

Some nights I would lie awake and think to myself: Is this real? Where am I? I must be having a bad dream. But I was really there, in Africa. I wasn't at home in New York, reading about Africa in a book, magazine, or newspaper article. I was eating, sleeping, and living among Africans, in refugee camps. I was listening to them talk about their lives and sharing in their hardships. I was connecting with them, seeing and feeling what their lives were really like. Slavery and oppression were becoming real to me.

After a few days, however, I began to experience a strange and extremely intense mixture of emotions - sadness, anger, depression - feelings so powerful I was frequently overcome with fatigue. We were making the long trip from the Boki-Diawe' camp in Wourossogui. I had been thinking about how kind and friendly the men and women at Boki-Diawe' had been to me, and I started remembering the faces of all the children I had played with there.

I thought about the abject conditions they lived under, how they were forced to survive in these godforsaken places in the middle of nowhere with absolutely nothing to do, no work or recreation and no community infrastructure of any kind. I thought about the filth, the disorder, the chaos that was their existence. I felt it in my bone, in my flesh,

How could the way of life of thousands of folk - industrious farmers and their families whose farms and cattle had been stolen by the Mauritania government simply because the were black and wanted to maintain their African culture - have been so violently uprooted and replaced by such madness?

Yet there I was, surrounded by some of the gentlest and most polite women and men I had ever met. There were people who had been tortured raped, and, in some cases, castrated. They had next to nothing in the way of possessions, yet almost each and everyone of them welcomed me into their makeshift huts like a long-lost relative.

All of a sudden, I felt dizzy, as if time were standing still and I was being swallowed up in it, all six-foot, one hundred-and-ninety pounds of me. Sucked into a black hole of intensity. Before I knew what was happening, I was crying like a baby.

In The Border Country and Other Stories
ANDREW SALKEY

In this collection the author explores the genre of the short story to the full. The diversities embrace a father as a single parent, with a mother who is mentally ill and a daughter treated as though she is a deaf mute, never touched or smiled at by others but her father.

In 'The Singer', Carlos decides not to migrate but to remain and till the land. Anancy comes to the rescue and helps in the banishment of apartheid, while mystery and the unexpected are imaginatively unfolded in 'Turret Attic'.

The title of this publication is also the title of one of the stories. Set in Zalapha, Nicaragua, near the Honduran Border it is the scene for the collection of a people in the region whose commitment to freedom and struggle knows no bounds.

'Literature Today' Journalist, **Peter Nazareth** writes a few words on Salkey's 'In the Border Country'.

Three years after his death, a new work by Andrew Salkey brings together and extends the strands of his thirty-plus books. In the Border Country contains twelve stories, the longest of which is sixty-six page "After the Counter-Revolution, after the invasion," which seems to be a realistic account of the murder of Maurice Bishop the U.S. invasion of Grenada, the return of the monstrous Eric Gairy, the attempts by the people to reassert their will, and their suppression by U.S. planners.

Salkey writes crisply, giving islanders the larger picture: torture in Chile after the overthrow of Allende, the brutality of the Contras in Nicaragua, et cetera. He fingers the British and American prime movers.

This seems cynical, and there is much to despair about because, decades after Salkey became the coach for modern Caribbean literature as critic, advisor, BBC interviewer, editor, novelist, poet, children's novelist, anthologist, things seem to be worse than ever.

Some stories are close to "magical realism" as one instance, 'The Poet' presents the notion of compressing the English of the island to "Tellurian Taciturnity." Magical realism in Jamaica lies chiefly in the web of Anancy, the trickster spider who came with the kidnapped Africans. Anancy is summoned by Caribbea and sent to South Africa to end apartheid in 'Anti-Apartness Anancy' but kept in the Caribbean to help the people in 'The Hole.'

Anancy stare down at this wagga-wagga confession, and nod pure so-so disbelief. He well know that Caribbea understand the 1913 thing but to hear it plain regretful from a salube suburbs person was something extra voops.

As Anancy flit off to a next part of the city, he considering that these apartness people and the murder government truly know what they causing to happen to millions and millions of folks. But, one conscious that guilty don't even ripple whisper.

Still coil up tight spider. Anancy flit plenty miles to East London, and perch on a beam in a house that having regular discussion about revolute or stay-same way. Revolute holds the night. Revolute hold the night big. Mind, hear, voice one.

Anancy hear that '50 was the time when the pre-dawn on societies happen. Beat up and arrest, more of that in '55, '56 ,'57 and '58, and then the murderation in Sharpeville. '60 and the stay home demo and the banning of the GGG, in '611 and the Sabotage thing, in '62 more beat up and arrest; the passbook protest. '64 when police shoot people in them Back: then they pass the Group areas tra-la-la-in '65 and eleven years of white bondage. State Prussian and terror, right up to '76 and the Soweto rising when they kill school children and other innocent folks. And then a next ten years with the same justice -lack and brutality and murderation.

Patrick Augustus has written five novels including the 'Baby Father' series and 'When A Man Loves A Woman'. The 'Baby Father' saga is one of the best-selling book series of the nineties and has established the author as a controversial and outspoken representative of all baby fathers.

Patrick is the founder member and official spokesperson for the Baby Father's Alliance, a pressure group for separated fathers. He has written and directed several plays and is a regular newspaper, radio and TV contributor. Patrick divides his time between south London and Tenerife.

A singer-songwriter and producer who has performed for the late Princess of Monaco Grace Kelly, the Sultan of Oman, the Sultan of Brunei, and actor Roger Moore, he has also supported Frank Sinatra and Tina Turner. Patrick is currently busy recording rap single My Teddy Bear with 'Coronation Street' star Bill Roach (Ken Barlow). The BBC are currently filming 'Baby Father' as a three part TV series.

WILLING AND ABLE

A man and a woman. Both black. Both wanting the same thing. Each desiring the other. Neither having to get up early to go to church.

It was a sultry Saturday night, so late you could

almost call it Sunday morning. The whole town was creaking in its bedsprings and resounding with the echoes of moaning and groaning. On a night like this, he shouldn't have been surprised to receive the full sensual experience. Considering the message he had left on the lonely hearts line, he should have been expecting it. In response to a similarly 'teasing' ad from a 'SBF', he had replied, 'I've got the ship, you've got the harbour, what say we tie up for the night?'

But that was three weeks ago. He hadn't heard anything back and had forgotten all about it.

Then she called late on Saturday evening, her voice purring on his mobile phone.

She apologised for the delay. Said she had received such a tremendous response to her ad (literally thousands), that she was trawling through them one by one. It had taken twenty-one days to work her way down to him.

"Better late than never," she cooed.

They chatted away. Sex talk mostly, turning each other on with innuendo, each contemplating what it would be like to grind the other, his free hand deep in his trouser pocket juggling a stonker growing longer and stronger.

"Here I am lying on my back wasting good time by talking on the phone to someone I've never even met when I'd rather be rocking steady," she said. "Why don't you come round and put us both out of our misery."

No sooner had she given him her address than she heard the sound of his receiver hitting the floor.

Traffic? What traffic? Even with the streets full of cars, it took him only minutes to reach her eighteenth floor Kennington apartment in his Porsche.

Hairspray wafted out into the landing to greet him. The door was opened by a woman with a big smile, big wide eyes and that 'something' about her that makes men agree, "I know what you mean about her."

His gaze rested longingly on her heavy breasts, enticing him. Those breasts. They were just as she had said. You couldn't help but notice them in that low-cut blouse. If you tried not to look, they simply reached out and slapped you in the face — anything to get your full attention. They had his full attention all right, for a full minute before he noticed her watching him watching them. He had felt uneasy, but he just couldn't take his eyes off them. There was something strangely familiar about those breasts.

"Are you sure you haven't been a guest on Jerry Springer?" he asked.

She must have been used to this kind of thing. You just don't walk around the streets with that chest and not know about it. Most guys believe that women with breasts like that lose their right to complain about having their chest stared at.

Her gaze turned to his crotch, checking out his package. She grinned. From where she was standing it looked dangerous! She showed him into the living room, allowing him a good angle from which to view her backside as he followed her. Talk about booty bounce! It was just as she had said it would be. She had a sweet sugar boom-boom, that was the only way to describe it. One look at that and men would go crazy — guaranteed. No two ways about it, this was the real deal.

Anyway, one thing led to another.

Out of the cracked living room window, the Houses of Parliament formed a dramatic backdrop.

He was going to be making love within sight of Big Ben! Stuff like that never failed to turn him on.

Her furniture was covered in plastic. The only art in her home was on her fingernails which were longer than her fingers. She'd been wearing a weave so long she'd forgotten the actual length of her hair and, worse, she had a bad habit of sucking her tongue as she talked. In short, she was ghettofabulous. But what she lacked in savoir-faire, she made up for in dimples and batting eyelashes.

She used the excuse of showing him around the flat to take him straight to the bedroom. To his shock and surprise, her wardrobe didn't have dresses in it, but every kind of adult sex toy imaginable. There were varying types of vibrators — rigid, hard and soft and waterproof ones. There were vibrating dongs and double dongs, dildos, male pumps, butt plugs, clitoral stimulators, clitoral and vaginal bullets, eggs and strap-ons, erection keepers and 'C' rings, non-vibrating clitoral pads, vaginal balls, massage mittens and feather teasers, handcuffs and leather penis attachments.

But all that didn't matter to him. He wanted so much to reach out to that big behind as it teased and taunted his imagination, that he didn't even mind that she didn't seem to know the difference between 'ask' and 'axe' or 'film' and 'flim'.

They flopped onto the king-size bed and talked for forty-five seconds precisely before getting naked. Butt naked. Ever seen a man undress in three seconds? That's how long it took him.

She wasted little time, either. He stared down at her womanly splendour as she pushed those chocolate breasts rolled in almond dust solidly against him, making him quiver. Then her hand dived down between his legs, followed by her head. She wasn't there long before he started moaning with pleasure.

"No rush," he cried, more to himself than to her. No way would he last at this rate, he knew.

"Would you prefer me on my back or kneeling?" she gasped.

He eased her head back and told her to lie on her back and spread her legs wide.

Wonder, she did exactly as she was told.

For a moment he sat there, looking left, looking right. He just couldn't decide, so he buried his head in the middle and began kissing her breasts like he had never fondled the like before, the tip of pink tongue on soft-hard brown nipples. Then he fumbled his way rather clumsily down below in search of that magic spot. Either he was way off the mark, or here was a woman who didn't have one.

Oh well, there was nothing to it but to do it.

It was a little tricky (he smiled to himself with self-congratulatory pride) but he managed nevertheless to ease himself in. Suddenly she stiffened, as a thought interrupted her euphoria.

"Supposing I get pregnant?" she whispered, softly and sincerely.

He didn't answer. What could he say? He was wearing two condoms, how much more protection could he possible have?

Anyway, this wasn't a time for talking.

"Relax. Just close your eyes and enjoy every minute of it," he said eventually in a soothing, reassuring voice.

What more could he say? That he had made enough mistakes and had been in this game long enough that he knew you couldn't rely on a single condom? Besides, he didn't need to tell her that, in the unlikely event that there should be an accident, she could always pop out the next day for a 'morning after' pill . . .

It felt so good he thought he was going to explode with excitement. He kissed her nipples. They were finger-licking good. He pulled himself out hard and stiff and eased in again, even harder, even stiffer. In out, in out . . .

It wasn't love, but quick sex. Just what he wanted. Just what she wanted. Excited. Inserted. Exerted. Inserted. Climaxed. Dispatched. Brief and efficient.

"Don't stop, don't stop," came a desperate cry from below. "Whatever you do, don't stop!"

So he put her on her knees and served her with grace.

And then he came again.

He grasped a gasp. He had never had a climax like this before. It was as if his stomach had erupted, sucking every last seed out of his nuts. Three hundred million soldiers, marching as to war.

And they just kept on coming . . .

All in all, it must have lasted a full ten minutes.

Ten minutes?!?!

Yeah, ten minutes. The whole neighbourhood heard his cry that night. From six streets away it sounded like an American werewolf in London. From five streets away it sounded like the howl of coyotes. To say that he was knackered afterwards is an understatement. Yet he was still as hard as a rock. He knew, however, that if he so much as even thought about it, his buba would snap in two. Just like that.

Unperturbed, she took his twitching piece in her

hand and guided it back towards her crotch.

"No, Shanice," he begged her. "Not just yet . . . I can't take no more."

He must have passed out, because his mind was a blank after that. He must have keeled over with a sly grin on his chops and fallen into a long and deep slumber.

In his dreams he heard an insistent banging on the front door. It seemed to go on for hours with a man shouting 'Shanice, open up this dyam door before I bruk it down!'

The banging and shouting was so vivid, so real. The next thing Johnny remembered was being woken up by the fierce barking of rottweilers.

Rottweilers?

Yeah, rottweilers. Two vicious specimens ready to tear him apart limb from limb at the word of command from their master, an ebony-skinned man dressed in black with a long scar running down the side of his face.

"Shanice, ah wha' de raas . . .?" the man barked as he grappled with all his strength to hold the hounds back by their dog collars.

"Oh, Cutty!" Shanice jumped up from the bed, pulling the bedclothes around her, exposing Johnny's nakedness to the world. "When did they let you out?"

"Never mind that. I said, who is this ugly geezer sleeping in my bed? Me did tell you seh, yuh nuh fe bring no man inna me yard!"

As surprised as Cutty was to see some man sexing his woman, he wasn't half as surprised as Johnny was to be present at the cuckolded husband's return. Not to mention the surprise of being confronted by two bloodthirsty killers eager to rip out his hood.

Johnny just couldn't believe it.

'This is not where I want to be right now', he told himself. He prayed to God that he was only dreaming. But he knew he wasn't. This was real.

He now recognised Cutty from the photos on top of Shanice's TV in the living room, right next to the coat hanger she used as an antenna. It was one of the first things he had seen on entering her apartment. When he asked her who the ugly guy in the photo with the 'telephone receiver' scar on his left cheek was, Shanice had said, "Cutty, my pickney daddy. He was a ruffneck from when him left Jamaica, so it never surprised me when he got done for GBH. But don't mind him, he's inside. He won't be troubling us for some time."

Cutty turned to Johnny for an explanation.

"And ah who you? Eenh?"

All Johnny could utter were the words "A friend."

"Friend? Friend?!" Cutty spat the word out as if it offended him. "What are you doing with my woman, friend? Me feel to jus' scar you up!" he screamed. "Me ah go let my dogs loose. Say hello to Satan and Lucifer, you battybwoy, you!"

Johnny saw his life flash before him. He saw his children and their mothers at his graveside, all refusing to shed any tears for the father they considered wotless. Why oh why did he not leave the premises immediately when he first saw the photo of that scarfaced psycho? Even on that underexposed polaroid, it was clear that Cutty's warped smile belonged to a man with a screw loose somewhere. Johnny thought about all the times he had been warned that his inability to control his libido would be the death of him. Now he wished he had listened to

Horny
R.K. BYERS

Journalist Steve Pope has called R.K. Byers an 'amazing talent that awaits discovery by the rest of the world'. His first novel 'Uptown Heads' was published by The X Press in 1997 and his second 'Horny' may just be the novel that gives him the props that he so deserves. A native of New York, Byers had to send his manuscript to Britain after being turned down by the big publishers Stateside. The USA's loss is Britain's gain.

<u>WASSUP!</u>

She liked his eyes. And not just the color, which she was sure all the other little girls had complemented him on to no end. She liked the fact they were open. They were wide open. They seemed to be taking in everything in a place where, up until she had seen him looking, she had been sure that there wasn't anything to see. He was with that asshole, Phil Flarn. And she wasn't sure she wanted to risk speaking to Phil Flarn just to chance an introduction. Then again, if she didn't speak to Phil, what were the chances they'd meet? Decisions, decision...

"What's up, girl?" a voice came up behind her and she swelled into a hug that seemed as welcome and genuine as the sunrise. Luckily, she knew better. It was Alanda, her girl. Right, she thought to herself with wrinkled lips. She hadn't seen this bitch in a minute and boy, did time fly!

"How you doin' lady?" Alanda asked. Quinn shrugged. That good, Alanda's quick flash of raised eyebrows seemed to imply an understanding. They stood there for a moment without speaking. Just nodding and looking at each other.

"Where is everybody?" Quinn asked finally.

"It's still early," Alanda said. Quinn caught Phil Flarn's eye wandering towards her, frowning. Then just as quickly as he had looked, he looked away. She frowned.

"How's the album coming?" Alanda asked.

"It's coming," Quinn said, nodding unevenly and going into the self-imposed terror that always seemed to strike her whenever someone mentioned, inquired about, or seemed to even be thinking about her 'album'.

Suddenly, her shoulder seemed cold. She was wearing a red strapped-tank in which her breast hung heavy like pendulums and swayed with each step she took. She had known from the beginning when she had bought the tank that it would give her a bizarre combination of pride and shame for her upper half every time she put it on. Sure, she loved her heavy chest, the way her breast seemed to be perfect, intimidating almost, but sometimes they were a burden. Sometimes they were a distraction. If she was making a point or voicing something she felt needed to be understood, they would be there seemingly mocking her seriousness. Lampooning her almost. However, if she simply wanted to be the sexiest thing in the room, there was nothing better than a pair of big, fat titties. The problem was, during the course of an evening she often wanted both sensations. To be taken in earnest and regarded as a hot sex object. Just what she wanted right then occurred to her as a breeze from something, the opening of a door? Sent a chill through her shoulders. She rubbed her upper arms.

"What's up Quinn?" came a dull even tone from behind her. She turned and found herself fact to face with an asshole: Phil Flarn.

"Phil," she said evenly, hoping he would realise that by saying nothing more she was neither greeting nor welcoming him. She was simply acknowledging that he was standing there and he had spoken.

"Seen my lady?" Phil asked monotone.

"She didn't come with you?" Quinn asked.

"Nah," Phil said, shaking his head. "I was supposed to meet her here. I brought my man with me."

Then he stepped forward.

"Quinn, this is Caesar," Phil said deftly. "Caese, this is Quinn."

"Nice to meet you," Caesar said a little unevenly and Quinn knew she liked him immediately.

"Nice to meet you too," she returned volley, looking into his eyes and deciding that yes, she liked them for both reasons: their openness and their almost startling emerald and bronze coloring.

"I told her I was gonna be here at ten," Phil continued, returning to the issue of his missing girlfriend as he looked around the still half-empty basement of a club. "She's probably somewhere with a dick in her mouth."

"Phil!" Quinn shouted, indignant.

"Goodness gracious," Caesar mumbled, trying to match Quinn's indignation but actually sounding just a little like he was really close to laughter.

"I mean, it's possible!" Phil said, turning back around to face Quinn and smiling because he knew that he had got her. He had rattled her.

"But that's my girl and I'm not just gonna stand her and let you talk about my girl like that," Quinn defended.

"That's my girl," Phil corrected. "She's your friend. She's only your girl if you're fuckin' her. You're not fuckin' her, are you?"

"Yes," Quinn deadpanned. "I'm fucking her."

"I knew it!" Phil snapped. "I knew y'all was into that shit! All you jazz bitches are alike. From now on I'm only fuckin' with hip-hop bitches."

Before Quinn had a chance to load up and return, Phil was gone, disappearing into a conversation with a bass player they both knew.

Quinn watched him, unaware that she was shaking her head and also unaware that he had left something behind with her.

"He was only saying that to bother you," Caesar said evenly.

She stared up at him, up into his beautiful eyes.

"That your friend?" she asked hotly, ready to see how he got down.

"All my life," he said quickly.

He had defended his friend, despite the fact that it probably wouldn't get him any points with her. She liked that.

"Why does he do that to people?" she asked, now simply trying to understand how an obvious lunatic like Phil Flarn could have someone like this pretty-eyed boy come to his defense.

"I don't know," Caesar said frowning. "I think he

likes you, though. If he didn't, he wouldn't have anything to say to you at all."

Quinn nodded, thinking that if insults were the price of Phil's friendship, she'd just as soon be his enemy.

"Does he talk to you like that?"

"Never," Caesar said.

"Why, doesn't he like you?" she asked coyly.

"Nope," Caesar said shaking his head. "He loves me."

"There is a difference," Quinn breezed.

"There is a difference," Caesar acknowledged.

"Dyke bitch!" came a scream at the other end of the room and both Quinn and Caesar knew without looking up that it was Phil doing the screaming and that Joyce must have just walked in.

"How could you do this to me?" the screaming continued. "I loved you woman!"

Caesar continued to look at Quinn. Even though Quinn was still watching the action, she could feel Caesar's eyes on her. She watched from the distance as her friend Joyce descended the stairs, then leapt from about three steps up into the waiting arms of that asshole: Phil Flarn. They kissed like they were alone. Then Joyce screamed.

"Who you callin' a dyke?" It was a high, loud shriek.

"Faggot-ass nigga!" Joyce continued. "You don't want me to let everybody in here know about that little thing you got for Kobe Bryant!" Phil looked terrified.

"You said you'd keep that between us!" he pleaded to laughter from everybody.

Quinn shook her head. There but for the grace of

God... she thought.

Phil and Joyce were walking hand in hand until they disappeared behind a pillar and were gone. When Quinn turned around, she was again face to face with Caesar. She was happy that he'd remained, but suddenly, she didn't know what to say.

"You know Joyce, right?" he asked breaking the ice before it had a chance to fully form.

"That's my girl," Quinn said quickly.

"I like her and Phil as a couple," Caesar said and Quinn gritted her teeth unsure of what she was expected to say next. It wasn't that she didn't like Joyce and Phil as a couple. It was that she didn't like Phil. Phil made anything bad. He could have carried the instruments for Miles Davis and them back during the Kind of Blue recordings and Quinn was sure that the album would have, in some way turned out different. It would have turned out wrong. Phil was a hell of a piano player, though. She had to give him that. And he was making one of her best friends happy. And he was here with this pretty-eyed boy.

"I guess I do too," Quinn said finally.

Caesar nodded, happy to have hurdled that obstacle and only then, for the first time, did Quinn catch him looking at the other two in front of them.

"You like those?" she asked smiling.

"Oh my God..." he moaned as she burst out laughing hysterically. "I mean..." he continued before pausing, "I don't wanna be rude or anything. But those are incredible."

Quinn grabbed them, cupping her hands beneath and squeezing, causing the already visible area of cleavage to swell in front of her.

"They're just titties," Quinn said simply.

"That's like saying a Benz is just a car," he moaned as she laughed. "Or Ali is just fighter," he continued as she laughed some more. "Or a diamond's just a rock," he concluded, giving her a chance to moan.

"I think I like you," she said as she regarded him with a slanted eye. "You know how to make a girl feel good."

"And I ain't even do nothin' yet," he said quickly.

"Quinn!" came a male voice from behind her and she turned, distracted and ready to end quickly whatever interference was gonna keep her from talking at length to this pretty-eyed boy.

It was Shaun. He was lunging across the floor towards her like he had something on his mind to let off. Quinn steadied herself.

"What's up, baby?" he asked, leaving way too much of his open mouth on her cheek as he kissed and made sure to sweep a backhand across her chest as he moved to hug her.

"Hello Shaun," she said flatly.

"Look baby," Shaun began, "You got any songs on you?"

Quinn frowned.

"I know what you're thinking," Shaun continued quickly. "But we're in the studio right now and we need two more songs to choose from before we pick the final twelve for the album."

"So what? You want me to come up with one for you right now?" Quinn asked evenly.

Shaun made his 'cute' face. The face he made whenever he thought he might have to use his sex appeal as part of an extra incentive. Somebody should have told him.

"You don't have to write one if you got one," he

110

said in his best FM radio DJ's voice, leaning with his fleshy body towards her as if hoping the top of his stomach might somehow graze the bulk of the bottom of her titties. Quinn leaned away.

She had actually liked Shaun at one point. Thought he was cool. He was a good enough producer able to collect some of the most talented young musicians around and get them to play together without egos. His ego had been his only problem. He doubled as a bass player and lately he'd been forgetting about his day job. He had actually begun to believe that he'd become a talented enough bass player with a big enough following to sell records.

He'd been pressuring people lately to play and sing on a new album that he was producing featuring himself. Now, as he stood in front of her, his yellow skin seemed effective in only making him look sick. His gut was neatly packaged in his black jeans and camouflaged in his black Nike sweatshirt and a black beret which made him look like some impossible cross between Charles Mingus and Huey P. Newton. Quinn didn't know which insulted her more; that he was only coming to her now to participate in his album, or that he was only asking her to come up with a song and not sing.

"How much is it worth to you?" Quinn asked, deadpan.

Shaun looked as if she had called his mother a country/western singer.

"Why would you insult me like that?" he asked, trying his best to seem hurt. "You know I'm gonna give you scale."

"Scale?" Quinn asked, incredulous. "For a song come up with right now? Forget it," she said waving him away. "I'll starve."

"How much do you want then?" he asked simply.

"Five percent of the gross royalties," she said simply.

"From the song?" he asked too eagerly. He had no intent of making the song a single.

"From the album," she said flatly. Shaun's eyes grew wide.

"It's only gonna be one song on an album of twelve," Shaun cried.

"That's why I'm only asking for five percent," Quinn said simply. Shaun looked thoughtful.

"Alright," he began. "But for that kind of money, I want 'Lover Man'." Before her eyes had a chance to grow to full wattage, he added, "And I want you to sing it."

"Un-uh," Quinn said, objecting by shaking her head with her mouth open. "Shaun, you know I've been saving that song for my album."

"What album?" Shaun asked cruelly. "Girl, you been making an album since I've known you and ain't an album come out yet."

How could she explain it to him? Better yet, how could she make him understand? The fact that her album hadn't come out wasn't her fault. She was working on it even as they spoke.

"Twenty thousand up front," a voice said from deep inside her. Her hand was actually covering her mouth. It was as if she was whispering it to herself, but in her speaking voice. She listened again for the voice but it didn't come. She seemed startled when she looked at Shaun.

"Twenty-thousand up front?" he cried out.

"And five points," the voice said quickly.

"Now wait a minute," Shaun said raising a hand.

"That's what I want," the voice said.

There was a pause.

Quinn wasn't mad at this voice. She just wanted to know where it was coming from. For twenty thousand dollars, she could do a lot of things.

"And five points," the voice said again as Quinn nodded her head.

"Quinn…" Shaun pleaded.

Quinn shook her head. Then nodded again.

"Come by the studio later tonight…" Shaun exhaled, and for the second time that night, Quinn was actually happy. She watched Shaun walk away and began to look around the party. It wasn't that heavily populated. Most of the revelers were jazz or music people and it amazed her how they all looked alike. The men all looked like rappers, bank robbers or poets. Except for the older guys. And there were few of those. She looked at the women, some as bold as jeans and boots, others in wraps and headwraps. Hip-hop was playing and it amazed her that some of the people in the party seemed to know the song. She watched the heads boppin' and as people scampered towards the dance floor she was struck with the sudden desire to laugh. That's Biggie Smalls! she thought. Do those people know that? She did, hip-hop head that she was, and fought with her own tongue to keep private. These people, she had always thought, would never understand. Hip-hop was supposed to be a bastard. She was the product of a good family: jazz. Well, at least, that's how some jazz people carried it. Some made it seem like there was nothing of substance except jazz. Every other music was of a poor father. And hip-hop, of course, had no father. But there they were, jumping all around to the one song she knew of where the late Notorious B.I.G. and the late Tupac Shakur collaborated on. And the DJ kept playing on the part where Biggie's caught up chanting rhetorically:

WHERE BROOKLYN AT?
WHERE BROOKLYN AT?
WHERE BROOKLYN AT?
WHERE BROOKLYN AT?

Just as suddenly, Quinn's eyes narrowed. What had been the first thing that had made her happy that night, she wondered, remembering that the deal with Shaun was the second. It was certainly not the goosebumps. Her breasts grew hot which meant that somebody was looking at them. She didn't search out the intruder. Instead she focused trying to remember what had made her happy. Then she heard a voice.

"Hey Quinn!" Joyce was screaming at her. Quinn was happy to see Joyce. She wasn't happy to see what she was dragging.

"We seen each other! We seen each other!" Phil Flarn protested. His fingers were in the vice grip that was Joyce's right hand.

"You saw Phil?" Joyce asked.

Quinn nodded. Joyce released Phil Flarn. He ran off.

Quinn found herself watching that asshole: Phil Flarn. Carefully. He headed towards the back of the converted basement that was serving as the party facility, to the bar, then stopped. He made a right and headed towards the back steps where there were two bathrooms and several opportunistic young men selling marijuana and ecstasy tablets. He disappeared past them.

When she turned her eyes straight, Joyce was still standing there and talking, thankfully because she was able to pick up the conversation. But now she remembered what had made her happy first that night.

Now it made her sad. The pretty-eyed boy was gone.

Caesar Brown was on his way to work. He worked at night. All night at a hospital. In the laboratory, analysing bacteria and shit. He wasn't no doctor or anything. Didn't wanna be. His job just paid the bills. He had a daughter to take care of and a mom - if anybody can ever really take care of their parents. Caesar was always searching his brain for angles. Tonight had been a good night, he thought, as his tires touched the Manhattan side of the Brooklyn bride and he began on his way to the West Side Highway. Phil Flarn had been himself, which was always good for some laughs if nothing. He also got a chance to see Joyce again. And he had met a girl.

He hadn't wanted to be rude the way that dude had been. That light-skinned dude with the gut that had intruded right as he was about to try and get the number. Besides, he didn't know the dude or the dude's relationship with Quinn. He tried to wait her out, but she took too long. He had to get to work. His only hope was that Phil Flarn seemed to know her. She didn't seem to like Phil Flarn, but nobody ever seemed to like Phil Flarn. She might like me though, Caesar thought to himself with a nod. Yeah, she might like him he thought again.

Quinn had settled into a chair. The chair sat facing a

small table that seemed to be portable but was actually bolted to the ground. There were booths lining the wall to her right. They were pretty much filled with people that had already gathered into their cliques and now sat talking and studying other cliques. Quinn looked up and watched the wanderers, people that danced or walked, taking a break from their clique or flowing in and out of several cliques, getting the whole experience.

The boys in dreds were killing her. She remembered how she had loved them when they had started. When they were new and fresh and rebellious. It was like that with everything, she imagined. She thought about Afros. Before Afros had become a staple they had been a statement. Their first wearers were revolutionaries. She remembered black hairstyles taking a break from politics during the jheri curl era, then they were back with basketball players and bald heads. Then those too became standards. Dreds had always been beautiful but now even those were becoming neutral. She wondered how long cornrows would last before kids would be wearing them in commercials to sell soda pop.

Quinn was smiling now and talking as somebody walked up and took her hand. She knew the face. She didn't wanna work hard enough to remember the name. The person in front of her didn't want to talk to her. The woman just didn't want to start anything by not talking to her. They knew who she was and if they didn't speak, a slight might be interpreted. It was known that it was better not to slight Quinn. Quinn nodded graciously to the anonymous woman at the show of respect.

The DJ lost all the respect he might have gained

from the Biggie/Tupac collaboration when, immediately after, he threw on 'Before I Let Go' by Frankie Beverly and Maze. It seemed as if he was gunning for everybody, but in a haphazard way, as in the fact that even people that might have wanted to hear 'Before I Let Go' certainly didn't want to hear it right after Biggie, and responded with one unanimous moan.

She wanted to leave, but it was too early to meet Shaun in the studio. She wanted an emotion because she was selling what she believed to be the best song she'd ever written. She wanted some ecstasy.

She got up from her chair and walked, smiling and nodding, speaking when necessary as she passed people that initiated her actions. She made it to the back where the boys were. She knew some of them. She was looking for one. He was there, with his dreds, by the men's bathroom on the second floor. She didn't speak to him, she just tilted her head to the side and handed him the rumpled twenty and five-dollar bills, and he dug into his pocket rather obviously and pulled out the off-white pill in a small, clear plastic bag. She rushed downstairs in search of a beer. She was sipping and on her way back to her seat before she popped the pill. When she sat back down, she was almost finished with the beer. No one had taken her seat. She was so thankful she could have almost cried.

It was a while before she felt the first rush, paranoid as she always was with everything: What if it doesn't work? What if it's not ex? What if it kills me? But when she suddenly loved that asshole: Phil Flarn, she knew it was working. Phil Flarn was beautiful. He was being good to her girl Joyce. That was cool. The world was beautiful. You could do beautiful things in it. God was beautiful…

Quinn sat with her arms crossed. It occurred to her that her hands were very near her breasts. She wanted to touch them. She debated for a moment, thinking of the club and the people in it and considering how they would feel to watch her touch herself so lovingly in their presence. So she decided to be private and turn a little to her right so that anybody noticing her touching her breast would have to be looking at her so hard that they deserved whatever guilt or pleasure they derived from watching.

Her breasts were huge. She thanked God for that right then. She should have never complained. She ran her hands along her hips. Her hips were slim. She thanked God for that right then. She should have never complained. She touched her face. Her face was smooth. She thanked God for that right then. She should have never complained…

She was enjoying herself. Loving herself. Loving God. Loving life. Loving. She had just sold what she believed to be the best song she'd ever written and she loved it. That song would be on an album that people would buy. That song would be heard. And she would be the one explaining it. She wanted to sing right then but the DJ, God bless him, and his inability to keep a flow going, was playing 'The Candy Man' by Sammy Davis Jr. and part of her wanted to cry. She wasn't sad. It was that the heaviness of all the love was becoming too much for her and she had to let it out somehow.

It was with all this in mind that she floated into the studio. Shaun didn't like the look on her face. The players all had their game faces on. This was work. And here she came looking happy.

"Y'all ready?" she asked, walking right up to the

mic and standing before it waiting for some sort of signal that she could begin. All these dudes knew the music. They were pros. Shaun looked at the technician and shrugged. The technician nodded to Shaun. He nodded unevenly to Quinn. She began to sing. When she was finished, her head sunk into her chest and she left.

"One take," she heard Shaun's astounded voice proclaiming over her shoulder as she walked towards the door. "One mothafuckin'…"

She closed the door.

The wind and night greeted Quinn like a friend. She wondered about a cab, a car, and a way home. She thought about walking; there from Manhattan, all the way back to Brooklyn, crossing the Brooklyn Bridge in the middle of winter just to turn on occasion and watch the lights of lower Manhattan glow. A cooler wind, different from the friend that had greeted her at the door, changed her plans and, before she knew it, her hand was extended towards an ugly yellow motorized bug with four wheels, four doors and a foreign guy driver.

"Fort Greene," she said to the cab driver, her voice reminding her of a woman she had just heard singing somewhere moments before.

"Take the Manhattan Bridge," she said before he asked.

The backseat smelled of stale humanity. She wondered what combination of living had produced such a smell. Were they white men coming from Chelsea Piers, thoroughly convinced that given what they could do now plus the advantages of youth, they might have really been able to become professional athletes? Where they white women fresh from a sale, deodorant and perfume now a memory and full of the funk that comes from shopping as an indoor sport? Were they young brothas that moved quickly and, therefore, had little time for stuff like cleanliness beyond customary simplicity of a shower a day? Were they sistas like herself, keeping the cab from completely stinking, but unable to make the smell totally pleasant either because of the smallness of their numbers? Quinn smiled as she thought that she was probably contributing one of the better smells to the cab, thinking about the next passenger and how, if that person knew what she was doing for them simply by being, they would thank her. And she would thank them, she thought, as she swerved back under the Ecstasy influence. Because God made them all. And God Bless them all. Everyone.

Dancehall
ANTON MARKS

Jamaica may be a relatively small country but it makes a big noise on the world's cultural stage. This is the island that invented a whole music genre on its own, reggae. The impact on the world from this unique form of musical expression has been enormous. From reggae came ragga and the seat of worship for ragga is of course the dancehall.

A unique experience, the dancehall is as important to ordinary yard people as cinema was to working class Britons in the 1940's. No book so captures the vibe of the dancehall as Anton Marks' ghettofab thriller 'Dancehall'. Working at Heathrow Airport during the day and writing at night, Anton Marks penned the novel over two years. A fitting tribute to the culture of 'back-ah-yard.'

Glyn Mabley,
Music Journalist

<u>DOWN IN THE GHETTO</u>

Walking down King street go straight ah parade,
De people seh Pupa Josey yuh nuh 'fraid,
No my bredrin you must be mad,
As long as me pray to almighty God

Kingston hot

Lawd a God
Ah me seh Kingston hot,
Mek me tell you seh Kingston hot,
Ri-i-i-i-i-ight!

Nighttime fell reluctantly over the war-torn Jamaican capital. Josey Wales' words were like a prophecy of things to come—they summed up the deep-felt fear and anguish that the forthcoming general elections seemed to instill in Jamaica, but in Kingston in particular.

The body count was 720 dead and mounting daily.

The desperate citizens of the ghettos were busy burying their loved ones, gun-toting bad bwoys and innocents alike.

Yet the Gold Street massacre still managed to shock a country growing numb to daily atrocities. Nobody had ever witnessed anything quite so appalling as this recent killing of a dozen youths at a waterfront dance site.

Tonight the residents of Pink Lane, a cramped back road in the Coronation Market area, were enjoying a welcome respite from the conflict. It wasn't the lack of sound that made the night so calm; the howls of agitated dogs and the wailing sirens of security force vehicles could still be heard.

What was missing was the constant volleys of gunfire.

Bullet-riddled walls and burnt-out premises lined the narrow lane, mute testament to nights of heated gun battles. The empty husks of homes and once-viable businesses bordered the lane on either side, with zinc sheets dividing the gutted buildings and cramped tenement yards. Most of the residents were taking full advantage of the unexpected lull in violence, and enjoying some undisturbed sleep.

Simba lay quietly, unmoving, snuggled tightly between his linen sheets and listening to Mama Christy's snoring. He watched his father getting dressed in the flicker of the lamplight. Simba's waking eyes took in the familiar room which served as his family's dining room, bedroom and sitting room all in one; that was the reality of living in the 'hungry belly' ghetto.

As Simba watched his father prepare to leave, not wanting to sleep, he thought about his mis-spent youth. At sixteen Simba thought he knew it all. He listened to no one but himself, and was proud to be labelled as 'bad bwoy'. As his crew 'bigged him up', he began to feel petty crime was the only way of survival, and questioned his father's motives for going to work every day.

Him a fool man, Simba had said, caressing his shiny black .45 special, dis ah de only t'ing dat can tek me outta de ghetto.

But that was before his bredrin died before his eyes from the carbine of a trigger-happy rookie in a roving police unit. His crime was to snatch a gold chain from two country folks. His sentence was death.

Simba was much luckier.

Looking down the barrel of a Kalashnikov, he stared death in the face for the first time. The panic that had ensued at North Parade had saved his life. But the mental scars of that day would stay with him forever. It was then—at that crazy instant when the bullet exploded his friend's chest all over the sidewalk—that Simba came to understand his own mortality.

He now understood exactly how his father could get

up at some 'bad' hours of the morning—against the backdrop of daily politically-motivated murders in the area—and do the back-breaking work of a fisherman; all for his family—for him and Mama Christy.

Now Simba's ambition was to leave the ghetto and to give his parents an easier life. The thought of vacating the decrepit, cockroach-infested tenement yards of Pink Lane and moving to the new housing developments in Portmore made Simba almost swoon in anticipation. His duty now was to support his family as much as he could.

Simba and his father had had many conflicts in the past, but the funeral of his spar two years ago had spawned a new sense of reality in his young head. And though he missed sparring with 'de ghetto yout' dem', 'badness and mix up' would have landed him in Gun Court, or worse—on a cold slab at Sam Issac's morgue. Becoming an 'Artical Don' deejay was his best chance of realising his dreams now, and he had dived into his new image with relish.

He had even offered to help his father on his small boat, something he would never have thought of doing when he was running it hot with his idrens. His father, who had been surprised by Simba's offer, had told him:

"One fisherman inna de family is enough, bwoy."

There was a slight chill to the early morning air. At about 2am Mr George flung on his old camouflage cap, setting it neatly on his spotted grey hair, and wiped his face with his weathered palms as though he was trying to smooth out his wrinkles. He bent over to check the bag with his fishing gear for the packed lunch Mama had prepared. He sighed, and something made him turn and look towards Simba.

"You awake, bwoy?" he asked, his voice a hoarse croak.

"Yeah Missa George, couldn't sleep."

"You too! Me t'ink ah only me have de sleepless nights." He walked quietly over to Simba and sat beside him. "Yuh see dis, yout'?" He pulled his jacket forward and grimaced. "Dis is not de life fe you an' Mama. But circumstances mek it so fe now." He focused his moist eyes on his son and placed a caring hand on his shoulder. "When some ah dem pastor tell you money is de root ah all evil, dem ah raas liar. Dis is de root ah all evil."

His eyes swept the interior of the room, a look of distaste on his face.

"No matter what you haffe do, widout hurting a man, mek sure dis nuh happen to you. Yuh understand me?"

Delroy nodded, a wave of compassion for his father flooded over him. He straightened and answered with as much gusto as he could muster.

"Dat nah happen to me, Missa G, me promise yuh dat. As long as breath nuh leave de body, me ah go mek t'ings better fe you both."

The old man smiled.

"I had me doubts about you, bwoy, I must admit dat. But you grow up fe de better, an' me proud ah you."

He paused as he stood up.

"You start mek a name inna yuh music business, able to even buy a bike fe yuhself. You done good. Now get some sleep, you ah go need it. Remember, you ah help Mama down ah market tomorrow. I will see you later."

"Lickle more, Missa G," Delroy answered, yawning.

Mr George left as quietly as he could, closing the door behind him gently, but their dogs, Rambo and Tyson, howled farewell to their master from out in the yard. Simba listened to the sound of his father going down the lane, then put his head down and sank quickly back to sleep.

Mr George ambled down the lane, his bag slung over his shoulder and his dirty hat drawn down over his eyes. The stark, uninspiring terrain ahead of him was poorly lit by street lights too far apart. But he had walked this way many times before, and it held no surprises for him. He was known and respected by all the roving 'gundileros' of the area and even though he did not want to admit it, he had taken root in this place that he wanted to curse every day.

Half way down the lane he stepped over a discarded tyre and thought he saw a movement at the corner of his vision. The old man rubbed his eyes, looked again and saw nothing, dismissing it in his mind as Miss Murtle's 'black puss'. He quickened his pace. Choppy, his fishing mate, would be sitting in the old Lada at the corner—no doubt with a 'bighead spliff' which he had fired up while he was waiting for him. He could just about see the rear of Choppy's old 'salad' in the distance, when a sharp metallic sound shattered the silence of the lane behind him. He turned to see several men in uniform coming towards him carrying M-16s and Kalashnikovs.

Mr George recognised the men as being from the notorious Hammond Barracks police section. Their white combat helmets and dark blue fatigues distinguished them from the rest of the constabulary. This was the government's Operation Eradication squad, a rapid response unit deployed to combat the rising tidal wave of violence on the island.

"Ole man—" one of the men called out, "—we come fe yuh bwoy! Whe' you live?"

The fisherman shook his head in disbelief, squinting and shuffling backwards, his eyebrows knotted in confusion. Why dem want Delroy? He had no idea, but he knew that these men weren't about to start giving explanations.

"What de raas unuh want him for? Him nuh live yah."

He angrily tried to dismiss their questions.

"You ah lie, ole man—an' we nuh have time fe no liar. I want you to give yuh bwoy dah message yah, an' nuh leave not'n out, understan me..."

They cocked their weapons.

BLAM! BLAM! BADDAP! BADDAP!

The gunshots startled Simba awake. He rose bolt upright. They sounded as if they had come from just down the lane. Had he dreamt it? He rubbed his eyes. How long had he been asleep? Was it a minute or an hour?

His heart was pounding in his chest.

Mama Christy stirred in her sleep but didn't wake. The night was silent again, but Simba was still anxious and lay tense listening for any sound.

All he could hear was his own breathing, at first— then he heard the sound of running feet, stumbling and frantic. Someone crashed through the gate and skidded to a stop right outside their door. Fists slammed on the shaky door frame.

"Mama Christy! Mama Christy! Fe God almighty sake, open de door!"

The Ranking shot out of bed in his shorts and string vest and pulled the door wide open. Choppy stood in the doorway trembling uncontrollably, his eyes filled with tears and his thick lips trembling with anguish.

"Him dead, man!" he bawled. "Dem kill him, Delroy, Jesus Christ him dead…"

He pointed out at the street.

Mama Christy came up to the front door still groggy and disorientated with sleep. But by then Delroy had tumbled out of the door in his shorts and was running in the direction his father took to work every night.

A group of dreary-eyed Pink Lane residents were standing in a circle—women 'bawling' wringing their hands and men running around helpless, like headless chickens. They parted as Delroy ran through, almost stumbling over the figure sprawled across the sewer, his dripping blood colouring the slow-flowing water red.

Hot tears streamed down Simba's face—he stared down in horror and anguish at his father's crumpled, bloody body.

Mr George was hardly recognisable, his body shattered with bullet holes. His hat lay near him.

Simba fell to his knees and sobbed as he had never done before, hugging the blood-stained body of his father.

"Dem kill him! De man dem kill Missa George!" Simba howled like a wild animal. "Unuh ah hear me! Whoever do this to me ole man ah go pay wid dem raas life! Unuh ah hear me, star?

"WHEREVER UNUH DEH, UNUH AH GO PAY!"

My Once Upon a Time
DIRAN ADEBAYO

Diran Adebayo's first novel 'Some Kind of Black' won him not only the Saga prize but a legion of fans. His second novel 'My Once Upon a Time' continues the themes of contemporary black Britain but his writing has grown more confident and inspired. He writes about ordinary people, but his writing is anything but ordinary. The vibrancy of black British culture mixed with traditional English prose is what makes Diran Adebayo such a fresh and exciting story teller. But don't take my words for it, take his. Rewind selector and read on...!

Steve Pope,
Columnist, New Nation

INTRO/OUTRO

The end was also the beginning in that they both involved this man and a note. Of course the man at the beginning was well, very well, while at the end he was dying a sudden, desperate death, but the note was the same:

One Man amongst a thousand have I found. But a woman among all those have I not found.

He lay with his arm outstretched, holding up his precious

scrap of paper, as hot burgundy blood traced their trails around like him. Like he was somehow trying to save the thing. And I can remember blankly wondering if the blood would reach and soil his note before his end, or at all, as the girl wept in front of me.

Then there was a tremendous roll of thunder. I turned to the window to be seared by the dazzle of red, gold and green, and I fell.

I often ponder on that last little question, now I have all this time.

A mystery man...could it be that I was finally getting overs?

I remember I was reclining in my office, throwing my darts at the board, daydreaming about getting overs, and all the pretty things there would then be for me...Just doing my everyday really, when the intercom buzzed.

I scoped the street from the window, but no foreign wagons or anything out of the ordinary down there. Could it be a bailiff, a prospective client, or a stink man come to step on me?

"Reality Ruless?" The soft burr of a brother came down the line. He sounded pleasant. Maybe he wasn't from these parts.

"Is what it says, don't it?" I replied. "Who dis?"

"I've come to talk business."

I said nothing. Give a guy a few moments to stew and he tends to give himself away somehow.

"Business," he repeated. "I have a business offer."

I buzzed him up. A client, it seemed. Who knows, maybe one with serious collats. That would be even nice. But never this year.

I draped a piece of cloth over my nasty, little stove, pulled some sheafs of paper from my drawers, arranged them on my desk, then cast an eye up to check that all my floppy disc boxes were neatly stacked up on the shelf behind me. On their sides ran the dates and initials of previous clients. They were mostly empty - noting stuff down was the kind of simp's move that got a man of my profession in trouble. But the labels spoke the language of efficiency to the punters.

I switched on the computer. Perhaps I should have sold or pawned this thing by now, but I was too attached to it. I spent a lot of time on the Net.

I pulled my bottom drawer out slightly, so my bucky and blade were to hand, just in case, and sat myself behind my desk, looking busy.

The guy stood a moment on the other side of my glass door. He ran his eye over its inscription - 'Reality Rules' - cos the city ain't pretty - before knocking and entering.

My man was six foot and counting, his hue a rich mahogany, and carried a good weight easily and evenly about him. He wore a cream crushed linen jacket with matching trousers, and a shirt of deep brown that had an expensive, velvety quality to it. Elegant, but not flashy. I welcomed that.

No doubt any hustler could have rented out some quality gear for the day. I did myself, from time to time. But all bar the champions betrayed themselves still: a scar or an excessive fondness for chapereetas here, an ill-concealed brawliness of presence there. But this guy! His abs looked solid but he wasn't shoving them in your face; he looked like he had hardly been feet deep in the strife but he didn't seem simple; he had some grace...yeah, class is the word. He looked like one of those broad-backed, top-track, supping with the big boys-brothers.

"Boy," he said, more a statement than a question.

"Do I know you?" I replied.

There was mild amusement in his eyes.

"I need an investigator. I would appreciate your skills."

His gaze travelled the room, taking in my discs, my dart board, designed as a map of the city, and my cabinet, where I deposited my bedding during office hours. He paused, as my more tasteful visitors tend to, by the framed print of a wry old sporting cartoon, The Evil that Men Do, before fixing on my knife certificates.

I had these 'defensive weapon' permits for every side of the city, embossed by the area's police authority, to be renewed each year. My profession was one of the few granted them. I also had a set of the fully-fledged Private Investigators' licenses, but these I rarely took about with me. Some fool out there might take you for an informer and step on you with a swiftness if they saw a licence with the stamp of the state. I only used one for my infrequent forays out west - the land of pukka postcodes, mansions by the load, boulevards for roads, and all that good stuff. Men such as I couldn't move a butttock down that part without all your papers being in order, but luckily the folk up there were largely ice-cream, the killers few and far between.

He went over to the wall to take a closer look and I welcomed his interest for, although hardly a man of means, in the matter of knives I could not be embarrassed. The regulation five incher that I showed to the authorities as requested, were just the start. In the bolted cubby-hole beneath my feet, for all things fight and beautiful, lay my butterfly blade, my blade of many switches, my Shaolin steel, my thin man's knife, my fat man's knife, my 'six pack? - No matter' knife, my rusty 'if the first cut don't do you, the secondary infections will' razor, my little late cut number, for when your foe thinks you're walking away, and never forgetting my treasure. My little baby. Its business end was three and a half inches, which glinted differently as the light caught it. Around its grip, in a sheath of intricate bronze thread, was woven a tapestry of some balletic, ancient battle. All that plus a nugget of a cherry-stud on top.

"I would like for you to find me a very special somebody," he said, turning to me.

"Aha. Well, special somebodies tend to require special rates. We may as well settle that side of - "

He hushed me with his fingers .

"You will be compensated for your endeavours beyond your wildest dreams, believe me."

Well, obviously I liked the sound of that. Although "compensated" sounded ambiguous - a trick term maybe. No way was I busting a leg for this man without pure folds up front.

He seated himself in front of me, his fingers brushing against all the dust on the armrest. He studied the soot in his hand, still his genial self, and relaxed deep into the chair, his right foot resting on his left knee. had not seen a brother sit like that in years. I continued to hunch slightly forward, my weight in my thighs and backside, ready to spring should there be any funny business.

"Tell me, Boy, what do you believe in, heaven or hell?"

It was the refrain to an old, popular song, first recorded, I believe, some time in the nine-zeroes. Folk still sung fragments of it.

"That's easy, I said "'We don't believe in heaven, 'cos we're living in hell.'"

"Nearly. That's nearly right," He smiled encouragingly, and fingered his silver ring. It had a black spider design for a signet. "And The Bible, do you know it?"

"The Bible?" I was a little flustered. I didn't want to lose this commission over a trifle. Scripture had only been an optional subject at school, and The Bible had jostled for our attention with other approaches. "I'm familiar with the old part. Exiles, betrayals, vengeance, battles, plenty of trial an' tribulation, I remember. As for the new, well I've never really had any need for it in my line of work," I trailed off.

"No matter." He fished in his breast pocket, brought out a crisp piece of paper, and pushed it towards me. "This is a little something from the old. Ring any bells?"

I scanned the note. It was written in a flourish-ful, calligrapher's style on fine, cream parchment:

One Man in a thousand have I found. But a woman amongst all those have I not found.

I shook my head and, much as I wanted to hurry on to money-matters, I held my fire. For he had posed me some quirky questions, which eventually might coalesce into a riddle. And I have long welcomed riddles.

"Let me explain," he continued. "I am a man of means. What can I say? Life has been kind to me. I live in the country. A large farmhouse that looks out over rolling land. Untold acres! I have fresh water fountains and tree-lined avenues, cherry orchards, fields of lavender, flowers of every shade and delicacy...."

Flowers! Did I look like a man interested in flowers?

"And when the trees trap the gentle west winds and blow them over the apple blossom," he breathed in deeply, no doubt contemplating all his quality shit. "Trust me, Boy, you've never seen so much pretty green!

"But you know how it is. In the country, there are few of our kind. You get lonely sometimes. We all have our needs, you understand my meaning? I need a queen, a woman from this city. A lady to treasure, to make my blessings complete. "

I lit a cigarette and looked at my watch.

"A lady? Listen, boss, I'll tell you this one thing for free. Why don't you just walk out of here, get to a bar or someplace, flash a few of your folds and maybe one of those flowers you're so keen on, and you'll get all the ladies you can deal with - "

'Really, Boy. You mock me. You know I'm looking for quality, a woman of substance."

"How much substance? Fat? Thin? Redskin? One with red cherries on top?" I jested. I was thinking of my knives.

"Oh," he shrugged. "All that is of no importance. Simply the lady who would like to take up my offer. The lady who would come to my little piece of paradise, wake up of a morning, smell the coffee, and see that it is good."

"Well, if you're on the real," I said, "let me warn you I don't do jobs by the hour, or half-days. This will be a full day's whack - "

"A day?" He laughed. I think we both deserve a better crack than that. I may be lonely, but not so lonely! A week, I had thought, should be sufficient, one way or the other."

He dipped into his breast pocket , brought out a wallet and let his eye wander, I felt a little knowingly, across my disc boxes. "Perhaps a cover-all fee of 100,000 would be in order for your full, speedy attention?"

He spread thirty folds on my table, each one a cool grand. I pored over them, I checked them, I believe I may even have smelt them. Forty thousand crisp, spanking, spring-clean snaps. What kind, crazy person was this?

"Forty now, for expenses, and to satisfy you of my bona fides. The balance on mission complete. "

I nodded. I could barely speak. A weakness had overtaken me. I even forgot to try and harry him for any more.

He eased himself up, gently patting his creases.

"I'll bring you a range, supes. You know, like a shortlist. Five, ten, whatever." For this kind of money I wanted to assure him value.

He shook his head and gestured at the note. "Just her."

He had taken my hand and was halfway to the door before I remembered what I had been meaning to ask.

"This girl. How shall I know?"

""Oh, you will know. I trust you. I'll be in touch."

And that was that.

I locked the door, stuffed his note in pocket, then contemplated this mad money in front of me, as welcome as pussy in midwinter. Yeah, looked like I was coming in from the cold.

I reached for my arrows and flung a quiverful into the left, west quarter of my board. Treble after treble. Could it be that I was finally getting overs?

2) Some Pit stops - Musings at the necessaries' spot

As dust stole over, I slipped my lucky silver coins in my breast pocket and grabbed my don't-leave-withouts: keys, phone, night-sights, and a blade from the collection. Underneath I'd fitted my light, laminated kelvar vest, a defence against cuts and caps from under-powered pieces such as my own antique Tanfoglio, which I eventually decided against taking: it was unlikely I'd need it where I was going and, besides, I was feeling lucky. Looked like Luck was being a lady to me that day.

And although I was way ahead of excitement in the race to the end, I must confess to a certain tingle then, over and above the money matter. For I would now have the opportunity to head out west, where I was sure this business could be swiftly sorted. I had lacked a reason to venture down there for a while. It would be like, yeah, a holiday.

I believe I may even have hummed a little something as I killed the lights, felt my way down the stairs and landings, and headed out the back way to my ride.

My vehicle was a vintage Cherry Datsun saloon. Its previous owners had painted the car with a long white stripe that gave it a certain distinction. But, in truth, my vehicle was something of a tank - its edges were hard and its snout long and broad. It wasn't pretty, but then neither was the city.

My street was quiet, apart from a few worker bees, scurrying to the safety of their vehicles or the public transportation.

They cast edgy looks about them every so often. The midscale mutinies that had triggered the imposition of the curfew and the appointment of the Minister for Special Duties, was at best the end of the beginning, ran the word of mouth. So folk were mainly sheltering against The Big One, surrendering the outdoors to the hardcore.

I liked to listen to soundtracks in my ride, tunes and incidentals taped from those old time pictures you rented out from the single-cigarette stores: the ones with martial monks from Shaolin Temples, swords and sorcery and gladiators, young guns and goodfellas, the odd brother with his hand on the steel, champagne, cocaine and much pain come the final reel.

That day I slipped in a thing written for Westerns. This particular project was put together by two out -of-state spaghettiheads, one Leone and Morricone, and should I ever come across them in this world I shall embrace them warmly. For Leone shot his men's faces up close, the way I liked it. Show me a truth - a virtue or vice - that doesn't reveal itself in a man's eyes. And his partner could knock off a pretty melody, with haunting harmonicas and plenty of space and sweep. When I started it up now, and listened to the grandeur of the accompaniment given to my predecessors in related professions, I must confess a sense of pride. The tunes made me feel large, like a knight riding out.

I turned the wheels round and headed down the side road that would take me onto the main. The west would come soon enough for me, but first I wanted to put into motion a little personal running.

The streets began to swell as I moved further south. All kinds of area boys and girls, their lives largely nasty and short. For there were six million ways to die and nigger mortis was all around but in the south they seemed to step on you just for the death of it. No rhyme or reason, riddles beneath the unravelling of them. Guess that's why they called this side the crime side.

I passed the chancers, the pram pushers, the rockheads, the clear and present danger-heads. Behind the bruised shop fronts that leant behind the 'Auction' and 'For Sale' signs, the single-cigarette-heads haggled for credit through the bars and grills.

On the road I saw any number of derelict vehicles - some with religious heads inside, touting window tags of 'Father Abraham', 'Exodus' and 'Not Today!'. But also the Mr. Friday Nights, purring past in their fancy wagons. They hooted plenty. Sometimes to hail up a bredren but more likely to chivvy the bus pass people across the road. Hanging like they were at the top of what passed for a tree in these wretched parts.

The inimitable rasp of the horn and the eddy of excitement that turned the pedestrians' heads could only signify one thing. Sure enough, as I rounded the corner, there he was in front - profiling in the passenger seat of his Jeep, three of his camp alongside - our favourite and most thunderous exponent of the gentlemen's game. Despite the evening's chill, the top was open and the tinted windows down, as the main man leant casually out, acknowledging the folk who hurtled towards him:

"Mas-ter Blas-ter!"
" Ay, Blaster! M.B, M.B!"

MasterBlaster dipped into the money bag that lay on his lap and, with an instinct for self-preservation so foreign to his style on the field of play, flicked out folds to all and sundry. Small denomination bills, I grant you, but largesse none the less. This way, no-one would come to rob him and his status as the People's Champion was assured.

Folk liked to speak proudly of how he still lived on this side. Although he maintained a place here, I understood that in truth he lived out west. But he always did a tour of the soil that bore him during the build-up to Sports Day, stirring up the juices amongst his homies for the match to end all grudges.

I felt suddenly hungry and pulled over by Nyam Food as the road bore left into the s. 10 division. The front had been granted a fresh lick of green paint. You hadn't really noticed the flaky dryness of the front before but, as soon as you saw the paint you thought , yeah, it could really do with that.

A few middle-aged care -in the community types were muttering by the door. Keeping warm, and seeking a sort of company, no doubt. Further in area boys, desultory, hands thrust deep in their pockets, dotted the walls. They kissed their teeth from time to time for two were serving twenty. What attention there was was being paid to a man who was defending his, uh, honour.

"Me nah come ah steal food. Me come ah buy food, seen?" he yelled stubbornly at the world, waggling don't -fuck with me- hands.

I understood he was getting grief for whipping slices of fried plantain from the side tray. Oil stains fast speckling his shirt front, and a drunkard's slur, did not help his case.

"Eb'ry day, eb'ry year yuh see me - ah you nah know? Tah rahtid! Eb'ry year, y'hear?"

The veteran behind the till, curled his lip and bided his time. I weaved my way to the front as Mr. Eb'ry Year grunted and flung a few inadequate coins on the table. I flashed a fat fold and told my man he could kill the change. Eb'ry Year shot me a keen glance, as if he knew me. I did not recognise him and I ignored his look. I was in no mood for words with a listing man. My server attended me and I was out with unheard-about speed.

Outside, I was chomping on my pattie when a police patrol vehicle, two at the front, two at the back, crept past. I fixed on the shards of glass that covered the pavement beside me - the remains of some unfortunate's car window, no doubt - and I was wondering if it was true that you could step through glass and fire without pain if you did it quickly enough when the same ride passed me again. I glanced up to catch the eyes of my keepers and was surprised to find a face that was female and young. The lady betrayed such a blend of fragility and hostility, that I assumed it must be her first day. The division had probably imported her from the west or even the country, in line with current policy. And although she would shortly be affecting the lives of my kind in ugly ways, I had to stifle a strange sadness. I tried to picture her colleagues conducting the tour. Question: what do they say to you on your first day down here?

Sunday's place was about half a mile further down, in this small, modern, state-sector development. The estate wouldn't quite make a You've-Never -Had -It -So-Good tour by the Minister for Special Duties, but you didn't do much better down here. And I welcomed Sundays his crib, despite myself being currently without one. He had paid his dues, and done as little harm as any after forty years on the crime side.

Elaine, the lady of the house and mother to many of Sunday's lighties, had just died. Of one of those antique water on the lungs diseases that had come again amongst us. He had married her in the hospital on the eve of her passing.

I had steered clear of the funeral earlier that day, having had my fill of slow-singing and flower-bringing. I had intended to avoid the afters do too, but my newly-acquired collats meant that Sundays and I could finally chat serious business.

Sundays was my weed man. Indeed, I would cheerfully have purchased all the necessaries I needed to make the load light enough from him, but Sundays was a man of inflexibility in this regard. He had no truck with what he called the poisons out there. His competitors had outdone him with their One Stop Spot policies but Sundays made up lost business with an eight days a week work ethic. Days was toiling in a garage, evenings were for his lighties, and serving a motley but trouble-free selection from the s.11s.

I had come to his aid once, as some static flew around with him changing supplier. His original connection, a man all kinds of slack who could not be reached until he rose at two in the afternoon, had suddenly declared that he would no longer take calls on Sundays. At this, my friend had finally lost his cool, raging against "dat lickle raashole! Him seh him don't do Sundays cah him rave on Saturday! An' you see how hard me strive, it don't matter what the runnings is! Sundays is the day the wise man get ahead..." And so we had called him Sundays from that time on.

"Ay, rudeBoy," Michael, one of Sunday's regulars, hailed me in the hallway. He may even have been one of the legion of Sundays' family. They bore no resemblance but I had never actually seen Michael pay for anything. And when a bunch of us were sat around waiting for Sundays, which was often, Michael would assume an official capacity, operating the land and mobile phones, and sending youths out to procure refreshments.

We touched and I nodded to his people before poking my head into the kitchen.

A girl sat, head resting on her hands which rested on the table, staring blankly ahead at two men focussed on their game of dominoes. They hurled mock battle cries of "Ai!" at each other as they slammed the pieces down.

Around them lay the debris of paper plates and plastic cutlery, the remnants of snapper, rice and curried chicken. Sunday's sister had begun dumping the rubbish into a black bag. To her right, Natasha, another mainstay, was monitoring a final pot of stew, and giving Sunday's daughter a lesson in dressmaking with a pair of scissors and tracing paper. Natasha's face was set in an unfortunate half-moon, her cheeks fat and long, her upper lip cleft and wont to tremble thickly over red gums. She was plain and poor, of no great anything. And I somewtimes idly wondered if I knew anyone with as little prospect of getting overs as Natasha. Who or what would rescue her?

But she was sweet-natured and, I understood, soft on me, and for this I teased her from time to time.

I came up behind her and gave her ample midriff a squeeze.

"Fix up a little something for me, ay, Tasha?"

Without turning, she stamped on my foot in mock irritation.

I looked for Sundays about the house, exchanging "Easys" by the bathroom door with a music promoter I had not seen for a while. The long crescent of his telephone receiver scar, the legacy of some troublesome negotiations with one of his acts, rose prominently as he chewed on his food. Age had not withered it. Behind him stood a second old acquaintance, fresh from the house of many slams, shaving off his bird beard (or the Beard of Truth, as it was sometimes called, in a nod to the celebrated growth of a local hero, unjustly incarcerated). Thick, tangled clumps dotted the floor.

A few like him apart, the gathering was mainly 'formerly known as' heads, submariners who rarely troubled the radar screens: guys of an age I hoped to reach, of some wisdom and a healthy fear, who had passed the peak hustling years, and now settled for the less fretful rungs of the local economy -

doing their trades, fixing goods electric or in wood, and cabbing around a community with no collats.

I finally located my man in a room upstairs. The room was barely furnished and a framed, youngish photo of Elaine, leaning against a solitary bouquet, looked lonesome in the middle of it. Beyond it, Sundays was surrounded by the usual suspects: Michael, Hope, a guy I knew by sight who today was suited up but who usually wore different styles of mesh vest, and a Latino, who occupied the honourary homie niche. Sundays squatted on the floor, the frame still trim and sturdy after all these years. He was tapping the laser display on his scales quick-time, and chastising Kamahl, the eldest of his brood. The son and heir seemed to have had trouble distinguishing his fractions from his ounces.

"Is wha' dat? An' how much you lose me, if me nah just jump on you? You nah hear of a sixth sense? Com-mon sense, enh? Mark you Kamahl, dis no time for larking about!"

Sundays turned dismissively away. "An' turn off the light in your room. It not a bloodclaat christmas tree!" he added as Kamahl slunk off.

I took my place to head nods and such, but only Hope actually got up to greet me. He loped over, and patted me exuberantly on the back with his good hand, so I knew he wanted something.

"Ay, Sundays, go easy on the yout'," Michael said. "It been a rough few days. "

Sundays sucked his teeth wearily.

"Him nah run with no discipline! Me haf to play both mother an' father now, and me cyaant have stupidness around me. Time to elevate the game and him nah see it yet!"

A thoughtful silence fell over us, as we contemplated the gravity of the mother plus father scenario, broken by Natasha's entry. She slipped me a tray and plumped herself expectantly beside me. She wanted to be flirted with, no doubt, but I was determined to finish my dish first.

"So, Boy, when are you taking me out?" she said finally.

"Oh, soon, baby, soon."

"Better be. Otherwise you're demoted. "

"How about next week or something? We'll go pictures."

"It's my birthday Tuesday," she said helpfully. "Come to my yard and none of your deep lateness."

Michael smiled as he watched the unfolding of the latest bout in our long established cut and thrust, wondering how I would extract myself from this one. The Latino joined him with a little cackle. He was one of those honoraries who never risked jeopardising his position by initiating a response or a comment, preferring to wait for the wind to blow.

I licked my fingers, and took hold of the bag of bush that Sundays had tossed over to me. The bush was in fine, grainy pieces, courtesy of his coffee grinder; somehow the draw seemed to last longer this way. "I can't take you Tuesday, 'Tash," I said. "That's your special day and your special man's got to take you that day, innit? How can I see you on your birthday and we haven't even started yet?"

As Natasha wrestled with a comeback, Hope begged a little piece-worth off of me. I wondered why he could not appeal to Sundays, but no doubt he was already deep in his debt. His eyes could not meet mine but darted around my body and my bag. Not because he was trying to salvage some scrap of dignity, but because he was someway ill and did not behave differently at close quarters.

My policy was to act ignorant when beggars threw themselves at me, although I tended to relax on this here, as etiquette demanded in one's weed spot of choice. However,

Hope was another matter again. This guy was so faulty you didn't even want him to owe you a favour. His simp thinking had left him with two fingers short of the monty, after he'd sold some joke thing instead of the Holyfield on what remained of our frontline. After that he'd gone missing until a concerned Sundays had tracked him down and brought him here, where Hope now hibernated, no doubt plotting another quality skank.

But my man had come for me that afternoon, and I had had two helpings of dinner that evening. I was, I guess, happy. I nodded and Hope snatched my bag and babbled like the brook.

"Yeah, yeah, yeah, yeah! Is all we have, you know," his good hand manoeuvred the smoke with a deftness born of necessity, "looking out for our bredren, idren, sistren still..."

Hope, the livin' clear and present danger head. He would have been better called Despair.
"So wha', Sundays, you expect you get another woman?" asked Mesh Vest.
"Mmm," replied Sundays distractedly, still breaking down, measuring and bagging his blocks. "Me feel so."
"What kind o' gyaal?"

Sundays stretched out on a rug opposite us, his head rested on an upturned arm:
"If she too chatty-chatty, me nah interested. If she too hunty-hunty, me nah interested. Me just need someone who can fit into dis structure here."
"Ah right," agreed Michael. "Someone who can help you keep t'ings ticking along."
"I'm on the lookout too, as it happens," I said and, after an apologetic look sideways at Natasha, furnished brief details of my latest case. And I welcomed this chance to let them know that once again I was in business and in demand. Matters had been rough of late and word would soon get

146

about that I was now living in my office. If you could only give the impression that your stock was rising then a hooligan might step on you tomorrow rather than today. And true, finding a girl was hardly the kind of manly pursuit on a par with my greatest hits but it was gainful employment nonetheless.

"A girl fit for a king in his castle. Me understan'." Sundays was intrigued.
"You get different, different volumes of girls," reflected Mesh Vest: "Smart girl, daffy duck girl, rub up 'n' ting girl - "

"Him nah want a girl like, say, one of dem Bedouin would have in their harem -" interrupted Sundays, " - concubine, yeah? When the man return from him field an' go 'Cha! Better give her a swift bash then!' Him want quality."

"You best fill up your tank and reach far out," advised Michael, "'cah the women dis side dem too hardback."
s"Ehnit though!" added the Latino .
"Me just like a girl that relax an' powder man so," Michael sighed,. "All dem hardbackers - me nah business!"
"If the women are hardback, you don't need to look far to find out why," retorted Natasha, "Granted, life run rough for both same - "

"I don't cut you, still," Sundays gestured apologetically in her direction, "but what it is, see, most of the girls dem start decent, Then dem get a man, maybe two or three. And what happen, right,eh, right yeah, is dem get bad man. And, from dem adopt the principles and perspective of that man, dem spirit turn, y'unnerstan'?"

"You lay wid dog, you rise wid flea," agreed Michael.

"Some women tink they can give you a lickle grind now an' then, an' that's it. Like using herself as a prostitute same way. Got to be someone who takes herself more than that, " reflected Mesh Vest.

MeshVest was being unusually vocal that evening. Normally, when topical issues came under discussion, he restricted himself to a shrug and an "It's the global, the whole basic, innit?"

"Don't look to her material look to her sensibility. You don't want a girl that can't give you nuff conversation. Why bother with it?" urged MIchael. "One glorious bash - it's no big t'ing."
"Ah true. But still the sexiest ones are the quietest ones," Sundays insisted. He turned to me, kind of confidentially: "Dem the ones who pour out the sex on you."
"A nice, loving, single lady?...Hmm. It not easy -" MeshVest shook his head.
"Dem too nice. Dem tink we're wut'liss, rasta, wut'liss! T'ink we're rubbish," Hope shouted, suddenly depressed.

"Because dem see right through you and beyond you," said Sundays. "Dem have ambition. You see a girl, you're all about the downstairs. But when a girl see you, an' check for you, most probably she'll think about settling down. An' that when the true problem can start, 'cos most likely you ain't even thinking about that... "

"That's it, though. Exactly." MeshVest slugged on his miniature rum bottle with resignation. "They're hard enough to find. But once you've got one, you can't get rid of her!"

"Me haf a girl one time," Hope buzzed about us. "Come back to the hotel now: a lickle dance an' business, a lickle advance an' business, nice, nice! Me nature rise an' me moving to undress her now, slowlike an', an'...me find tings. The girl haf tings!" He pointed at his own tackle. "Me jus' box the girl so and kick him boombaclaat out!..."
We creased up as Hope admonished, 'Watch out for the Lady Boys dem!" Hope always had an endless stream of tall stories

which he trotted out with relish and the merest twinkle. What with his recent steep decline, I had forgotten how droll he could be.

Kamahl took advantage of the cover to return. He switched on the box and settled himself beside me, as I suspected he would.

I found the thoughts of Sundays and his people noteworthy but could not count on their relevance. What knowledge could they possibly have gained of premier league ladies in their strictly southside lives? I myself had little form in the matter. Oh, I had dabbled for a period, but I found I rarely welcomed the whole wearying business of intimacies with women. Most of the time now, when surplus built up, I went out and paid for its release.

"Boy", Kamahl nudged me, "you don't need an assistant yet?"
"You finish school, and we'll see,"
"I don't do school no more."
"Is it?"
He nodded. I asked him about a computer firm that I knew he had spent a placement at but there had been no vacancies there. I was concerned. Not because he had left his school - by all accounts a rubbish one. But now there was nothing between him and the struggles of men and, like his father, I feared that he lacked the robustness for them. He still sucked his thumb when he could.

"So you can't do nothing for me? "
"I'm sorry, youngblood. Maybe soon."
"Show me some skills, then. One o' dem bad, extreme prejudice moves."
I sighed. "Not now. Another time!"

Kamahl was forever plying me with requests, mainly to provoke anecdote and instruction. And so I would advise him on cards and car culture, or embellish accounts of memorable cases. Most of all though, he liked me to retell the story of my arrival in these parts.

The circumstances and whereabouts of my birth remained unclear, but my mother later spoke of the night they found me, only a few months in, wrapped in swaddling clothes inside a grocer's bag, and lying in a doorway. A noisy bundle, I imagine. Certainly, I did something to attract the attention of the couple who now stood above me.

"Is it a boy or a girl?" asked the man.
The woman tugged at my tings.
"It's a boy."
"Oh, then let it be called 'Boy'."

Our introductions completed, they took me in and gave me a home, in the general way. And alhough, I was found deep in the city, I like to think, and have often maintained, that I was abandoned there after a start in the country. How else could I explain my slight sentiment for that lady officer and weak people like Kamahl, or my fondness for red cherries?

"So, you haf any ideas? A sniff for someone?" asked Michael.
I shook my head.
"Why don't you go look up the Race Man? Me hear seh him in town."

I smiled at the news. It did not surprise me that he should arrive at this point of general ill-omen. The Race Man did not come when you called, but he was always on time just the same. No doubt he would already be knee-deep in consultation as suppliants sought salvation in the one place where they did not have to face the judgement of their peers. But you had to husband your appeals: you were only permitted three pitches to him in a lifetime. And even then, he was wont to answer your question with a question, or else a deep riddle. Some insisted that we needed a Wise One who was more hands-on, or who at least had his authority recognised by the State, but they grumbled quietly for - despite his infrequent attendance, it was understood that his ears and eyes were everywhere.

I was yet to take up any of my dispensation. But despite this, and the evidence of the disappointed, I felt someway close to an appreciation of his ways and was certain that the key to gaining satisfaction lay in the phrasing of the question. No doubt we would link up once everything was ready.

"Me see him one time, an' boy! -" said Hope, eyes twinkling, "the brother deep. See Sundays - " He pointed to Sundays' three foot-long mane, " - all o' dat is like a single lock on him head! Him tell me seh him the Original Dread from Planet Zion."
"You lie!" challenged Michael. "Ain't no-one actually seen him. Man an' man say all you see is shadow and smoke. Lots of smoke."
"Yeah yeah," Hope took the objection in his stride," him puff a serious Planet Zion chalice. "
"Where you see him?" scoffed Natasha

"On the street dere. Just the other day. Wha' - live, I'm telling you! I was walking along - taking my mornin' constitutional an', an' this Merc park up an' my man step out. Him hol' a staff in front of him like so," Hope rose to reenact the scene, "and him covered in robe an' a big greybeard that stretch down so. An' him turn to me and rumble, "I have seen many things." Him voice like thunder! Me know seh him The DonDadda cah me bones just start to rattle - "

"Is wha' you aaks him, when you see him?" Michael tested.

He had been cued up neatly but Hope was flummoxed for an instant.

"We reason that day, bredrin. Philosophy, the State, everyt'ing an' everyt'ing. We talk about law: batty law and ganja law. How can batty be legal and ganja illegal, enh? How can man fuck man an' ladyboy up there and the police dem nah interfere, but still police come an' start wit' we? What kind o' State we livin' in?" Hope thudded the point home as we cracked up again.

"Race Man come an' go as him feel," groused MeshVest. "Cho! Him nah care fe we."
Sundays hushed him.
"Me hear seh him a Marabout - like the ruggedest, baddest obeah man," said Michael.

"What it is, see, he's a man, who, like, fed himself right," Natasha insisted. "You know how we try an' feed our body in every which way and it never enough? 'Cos what we really need to satisfy is the soul, and that's hungry still, y'unnerstan'. Feed the spirit and the body will... will alright, you know."

"That's more like it," I struggled to articulate my instincts. "We've all got what he's got within us. He's just a man that's made himself more refined than the rest of us. He learns stuff, and throws away stupid stuff, so he's constantly moving up the chambers. His overstanding and his endless purification of his insides is what gives him his wisdom. It's like every cycle is bigger and better than the last, takes him higher and closer to nature. So that now he's as old as the hills, and can harness all that power out there. It's like boxing. You don't catch a fighter sexing before a fight, or drinking his head off. He's gotta triumph over temptations, an' just sip nutrients and carrot juice an' all that, innit? Same way with the Race Man. Every day for him is like the eve of the big fight. "

Hope tried out some boxing moves on the Latino as Kamahl touched my arm.

"If you go see The Race Man, bring back a blessing for me,"

he said quietly.

I promised him I would, although I was not sure that the Race Man did blessings, then took my goods, said my goodbyes and beckonned Sundays outside.

With him seated beside me, I pulled my car round to the side of his home for some concealment.

"So what's today's mathematics, cuz?"

"Bwoy, famine ah lick still." He shook his head. "Everyone's waiting on sess and most of what I can get, or leastways afford, is just commercial. And now Sports Day come up, right - "

"You going to that?"

"Definitely. The touch that everytime. "

"Yeah."

"But you know dem style! They're hanging on to what they have, waiting for maximum hunger to mount, then make their killing. Tch! I ain't making money serving people no more, you know."

I knew he was speaking true. Footsoldiers like Sundays did not enjoy times of famine and inflation either. Their cost prices soared and they couldn't make real dividends. Only the big boys would be laughing.

"They're trying to change round the market, isn't it? Cheaper buying bones these days," I said.

Sundays nodded bitterly. "Me can't stand it much longer."

"Just give me as good as it gets."

"Low grade, you're talking bush at 120, sticks and that gummy silver at 180. Indica and sess 200 plus - "

" Ks, sir, not ounces."

"Wha'? You find a big pot of gold?"

I reached down, felt inside my right sock for the bundle of notes that I had taped to my leg, and handed them to him.

"That's 15 fat ones there, some of the advance my client gave me. I want you to buy me up as much as you can. No need to fret, I won't be troubling your neck of the woods, an' 13% goes your way at anything over 10 Ks."

He looked at me intently as I fired a cigarette, and gazed at the windscreen, and the dark beyond.

"Look, bro, this whole messed-up manor is about to blow - we both know it. Curfew, and famine now, plus all this politician talk about prosecuting the peace. " I turned to him. "It's gonna get worse and it's gonna get worst about here."
"Ah true."
"I'm getting out, dread, I'm sorry. This is it, this is my ticket right here. I'm gonna get this girl, collect on the balance, and then retire. Dunno. Even move out west, if things run sweet. Invest in this thing, then kick back and relax while I wait on bigger plans."

Two guys took up residence by the shops ahead of us, their hands in their coat pockets, getting their hustle on.

"Yuh see them with their street dreams!" I sneered. "Gotta hustle in the boardroom, cuz. Like you were saying, elevate the game. Check it. Down here, you get long-time lockdown. Out west now, if even they get you, you'll be loungin' in some open, leafy resting-home for a few months. Long dick-style - barbecued wings with all the trimmings, an' hot cherry pie for afters!"

Sundays chuckled. "I'm with you, Boy. You get the chance, you gotta get overs."
"No question."
"But you still haf to find the girl dat fit the slipper! Fe real..."
 He looked thoughtful. "You know, most women, they wanna be the First Lady to something. Now your client sure sound like something. And you too, yeah, right, you gotta come like something, to bring them in, y'unnerstan?"

He eased himself out of the car, then leant down at the window and patted the wad: "Nah worry about this. Come check me in a couple of days, y'hear?"

"You think you can handle it?"

He nodded and touched my fists: "Pro-tection!"

"Alright, then. Mind how you go, yo!"

"Give t'anks," he urged, in righteous fashion, and watched as I swung the ride round and pulled away.

One final pit stop. With Sundays' words in my ears as much as anything, I upgraded my wheels at Sammy's, to a crimson nine series Beemer A touch flashy, possibly, but when in Rome and all that. I told him that I would be back for my Datsun in a couple of days. He all but collapsed, gurgling and such, as I produced G notes without fuss and held them to the light to prove they were the Holyfield.

Back on the road, I barely noticed the whirr of the helicopters up above, or the thumbing pedestrians, hoping to secure a lift to their places of rest before the curfew hour, for my head was set on the west.

To order any of the books featured in this sampler, email: vibes@xpress.co.uk for details.

Sorrelle
Published by Livewire
£4.99

Promised Land
To be published by The X Press
£6.99

Orange Laughter
Published by ARP
£8.99

Brixton Rock
Published by Black Amber Books
£6.99

Healing Strategies For Women At War:
Seven Black Women Poets
Published by Crocus
£6.95

Drops of This Story
Published by Harlem River Press
£11.99

Changing Britannia
Published by New Beacon Books
£12.99

Bittersweet
Published by The Women's Press
£9.00

Wheel & Come Again
Published by Pepal Tree Press

In The Border Country and Other Stories
Published by Bogle L'Ouverture
£12.95

Silent Terror
Published by Harlem River Press
£9.99

My Once Upon A Time
Published by Abacus
£9.99

Dancehall
Published by The X Press
£6.99

Horny
Published by The X Press
£6.99

Who's Been Sleeping In My Bed?
Published by The X Press
£6.99

Dead By Popular Demand
Published by The X Press
£6.99